List of symbols

 maths skills

 connections

 groups

 puzzles

 geometry

 metric system

 arithmetic

 logical reasoning

 vocabulary

 writing

 spelling

 language play

 grammar

 comprehension

English version translated and edited by Maureen Spurgeon

All about me!

Can you introduce yourself by answering these questions?

I live at

....

My name is

....

....

I like playing

....

....

....

I like to eat

....

....

I was born on

....

My favourite colour is

....

The name of my school is

....

Objective: to answer a set of questions accurately.

The fairground game

123 There were 15 tins to be knocked down in each pile. Write the number remaining in each pile and this will be the fraction (part of the 15) which is left.

123 There are always 15 tins in each pile to start with. Using the fractions below, draw in the tins which you have not been able to knock down.

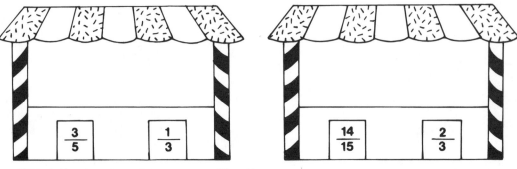

$\frac{3}{5}$ $\frac{1}{3}$

$\frac{14}{15}$ $\frac{2}{3}$

Objective: to understand the concept of fractions.

Odd one out

 Can you find the word which does not belong in each line? Write it down!

find, put, book, play, buy ....

cup, board, machine, pigs, bottle ....

apple, pear, tulip, peach, plum, banana ....

Andrew, Julie, London, king, Belgium ....

pretty, strong, big, beautiful, trousers ....

ball, call, festival, hall, fall ....

your, because, his, their, her ....

 Now write your own list of words with an odd one out in each case. Write the words on each line.

Verbs (action words) ....

Nouns (names of things) ....

Adjectives (describing words) ....

Words of three letters ....

Names (Proper Nouns) ....

Objective: to learn to recognize the common element in a group of words.

The stars

Complete all the sums on this page! The answer to each one is written in the centre of the star.

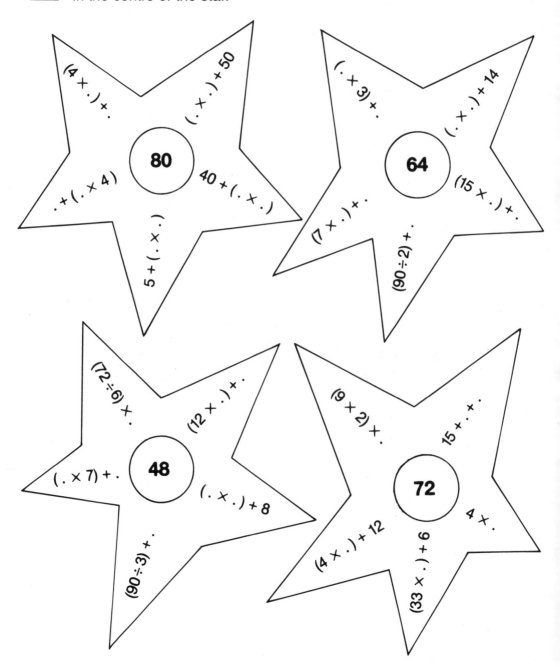

Plurals of nouns

 One thing is singular. More than one is plural. Each thing is a noun. First, write the noun below each picture. The first letter is written for you.

n..........................　h..........................　f..........................　m..........................　t..........................

Now write the plurals for each one of the words above.

.........................., ..., ... ,.........................., ...

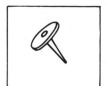　　　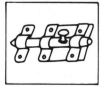　

n..........................　o..........................　j..........................　b..........................　k..........................

Can you write the plural for each of these nouns?

.........................., ..., ... ,.........................., ...

b..........................　c..........................　c..........................　b..........................　c..........................

These are all singular nouns! Can you write the plural?

.........................., ..., ... ,.........................., ...

Objective: to define nouns and plurals.

The school trip

? Try answering these questions and writing down the correct answers.

Before the journey, our teacher tells us the train will have 5 carriages. But Colin has seen one which has ten carriages more.

How many carriages does the train have which Colin has seen? ....

The big day arrives! The driver tells us that the 5 carriages are numbered, beginning with number 705.

What is the number on the last carriage? ....

The 25 children in my class get into one carriage. 5 people can sit on each long seat.

How many long seats are needed for all the children? ....

Sarah decides to celebrate her birthday on the train. She gives out 24 cakes and eats one herself. There are 10 cakes left.

How many cakes did she have to begin with? ....

When we arrive at our destination, there are 10 railway tracks going into the station. In one hour, 8 trains arrive in the station on each track.

How many trains arrive altogether in one hour? ....

Objective: solving mathematical puzzles.

In the plural!

 Here is a short story. Can you put each noun into the plural?
Remember – your story must still make sense!

The boy is eight years old. He loves playing in the woods! His best friend is a great, big, black dog. Every morning, he takes the dog out for a nice, long walk. The boy throws a stick for the dog. 'Bring it to me!' he cries. The dog runs and brings back the stick in his mouth. 'Well done!' says the boy. 'You are a great dog! You deserve a big bone!'

....

....

....

....

....

....

....

....

....

Objective: to change an extract of text into the plural.

Railway tracks

Draw three railway lines using the dots as a guide. Make sure the trains don't go off the rails!

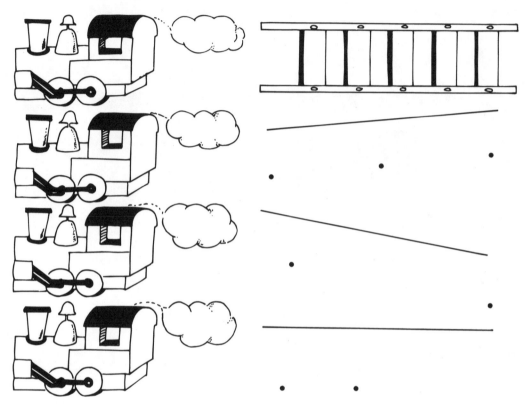

Try the sums on each line, following the direction of the arrows. The first sums have been done for you.

−9

434	688	695	762	627	758	399	106
425							

+7

444	469	166	496	332	996	211	104
451							

Objective: to draw parallel lines; to practise addition and subtraction.

Past, present and future

 Verbs (action words) are used in different tenses – such as the past, the present and the future. Here are two lists of verbs. Join each present tense with its past or future tense.

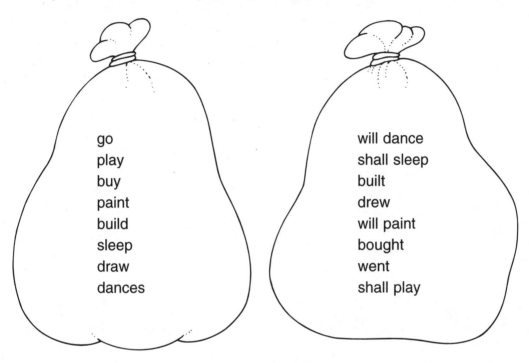

go	will dance
play	shall sleep
buy	built
paint	drew
build	will paint
sleep	bought
draw	went
dances	shall play

 Now write the verbs in the correct tense under each heading.

yesterday	today	tomorrow

Objective: to understand the verb tenses and use them correctly.

The archery range

If you can work out the fraction sums, you will be able to put all the marks on the target! Look at the example before you begin.

of

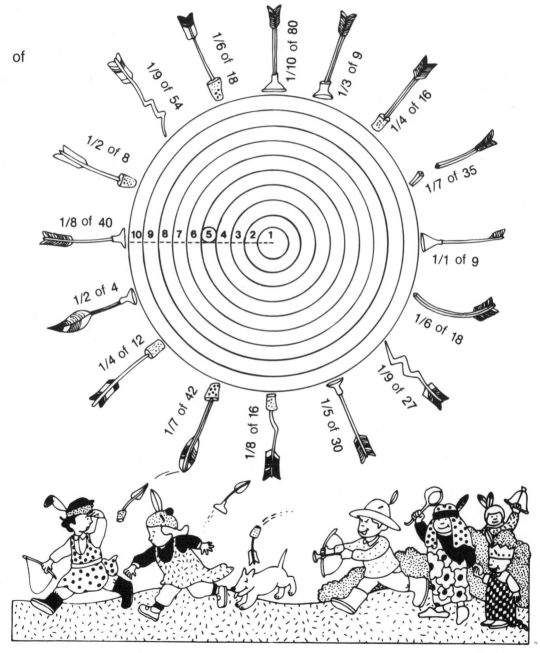

Objective: to work with fractions.

Help with your spelling

Parts of words may sound the same, but they are spelt differently. This exercise will help you with the right spelling.

First, the sound 'c'. This can be written, 'c', 'k', 'ch' or 'ck'. Write all these words in the correct box.

cat, kitten, cupboard, luck, orchestra, kilo, count, tick, character, case, ketchup, chemist, king, mocking, ducks, chrysanthemum.

c	....	ch	....
	....		....
k	....	ck	....
	....		....

The sound 'n' can be written in four different ways – 'n', 'nn', 'kn' or 'gn'. Can you write in the missing letters to complete the words in this postcard message?

Dear Joh_

Still _o sig_ of su_ _ y weather, but
it's such fu_ with my Gra_ . She
_ _ ows just what I like for di_ _ er
and she bought me a _ ew
pe _-_ _ife and a _ _ome for her
garde_. A _ _ at bit my _ _ ee o_
Su_day, but I did _ot care. See you
o_ Mo_day. Your mate, Da_iel

Objective: to recognize different ways of spelling parts of words which sound the same.

Hot or cold?

 At the centre of this scale is 0 (or zero). To the left, the temperature is minus (-) zero, to the right it is above (+) zero. Can you complete the scale?

|—————————|—————————|—————————|———¹————|———⁰————|—————————|—————————|—————————|

123 Now try this scale. The temperature is measured in units of ten (10, 20, 30) degrees (°).

|——|——|——|——|——|——|——|——⁰——|——|——¹⁰——|——|——²⁰——|——|——|——|

123 Look at the temperature on each thermometer. Then fill in the correct figures.

1° colder = ...°
1° hotter = ...°
3° colder = ...°
2° hotter = ...°
2° colder = ...°

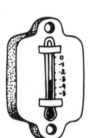

3° hotter = ...°
1° colder = ... °
1° hotter = ... °
2° colder = ...°
2° hotter = ...°

123 Colour each country in a different colour. Then colour the right thermometer in the same colour.

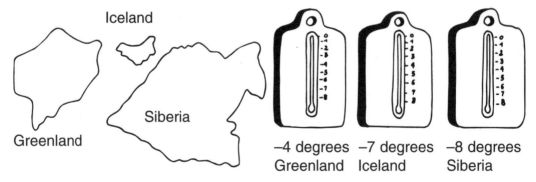

Iceland

Greenland

Siberia

−4 degrees −7 degrees −8 degrees
Greenland   Iceland   Siberia

Objective: to understand sub-zero temperatures and complete a graduated scale.

The alphabet

 There are 20 words below. Can you put them into alphabetical order?
Write the numbers 1-20 on the flags as you work.

Then write out the alphabet. a,_,_, d,_,_,_,_,_,_, k, l,_,_,_,_,_,q,_,_, t,
_,_,_, x,_, z.

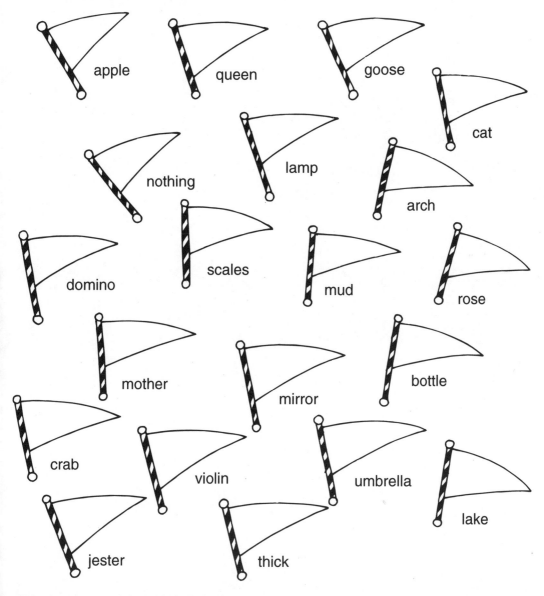

Objective: to put words into alphabetical order.

I can tell the time!

123 Look carefully at these clock faces. What time are they showing?

before noon (a.m.)

after noon (p.m.)

It can either be 7 o'clock in the morning (7 am) or 7 o'clock in the evening (7 pm). The hands are in the same place, but there are 12 hours in between. 7 pm can also be written in 24 hour clock as 1900 hours ie 0700 hours + 1200 hours = 1900 hours.

123 Draw the hands on each of these clocks to show the correct time.

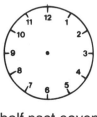

half past seven

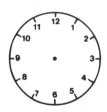

five o'clock

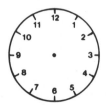

half past nine

1530

1930

2300

Objective: to learn to tell the time.

Making words

A syllable is part of a word. Each syllable on the left can be joined with a syllable on the right. Join up the right syllables then write the words.

car	den	don	bag	pan	bird
rail	ton	gar	way	black	fish
ma	key	gold	cake	hand	gic

....

....

....

win	lad	slip	osk	fire	pet
ki	work	car	mill	eye	dow
sa	cil	pen	brow	wind	pers

....

....

....

din	cel	mit	er	play	ain
cac	ing	gob	tus	trump	ner
par	ten	teach	lin	fount	et

....

....

....

Objective: to learn how syllables form words.

So many balloons!

The total number of points shown on all the balloons on this page is 1,000. Add the points together on the ballons which are floating into the air, out of Jane's hand.

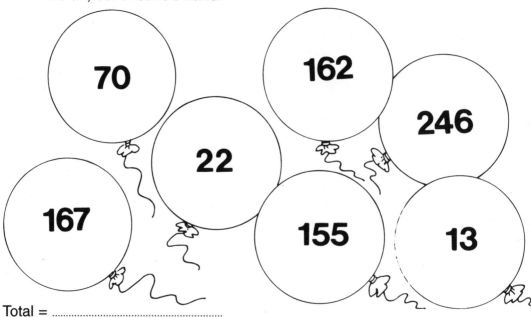

Total = ...

Add the points on one loose balloon to the points on one of the balloons in Jane's hand. The points must add up to a number which can be divided by 10. Give two possibilities.

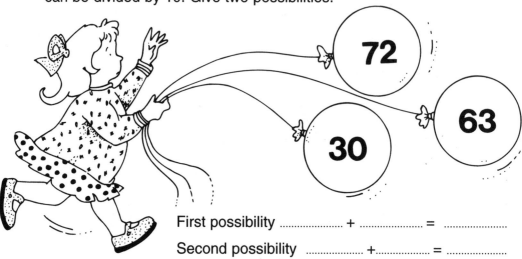

First possibility .... + ... = ...

Second possibility .... +................... = ...

Objective: to learn to add up.

Connections

Join the pictures to the words they are connected with. The first one has been done for you.

nail
scarf
nut
paper
autumn
hair
perfume
bottle

Which words go together? Each word in the box must be used twice.

transport	instrument	furniture	flower
clothing	tool	animal	tree
job	liquid		

doctor...

train...

violin..

screwdriver..

piano...

lemonade...

primrose...

bus..

dog..

wardrobe..

water..

birch...

oak...

trousers...

cat..

teacher..

bed...

hammer..

sock...

tulip..

Objective: to discover different connections between words.

Off to the beach!

To find the right answers, simply follow the arrows and use the key.

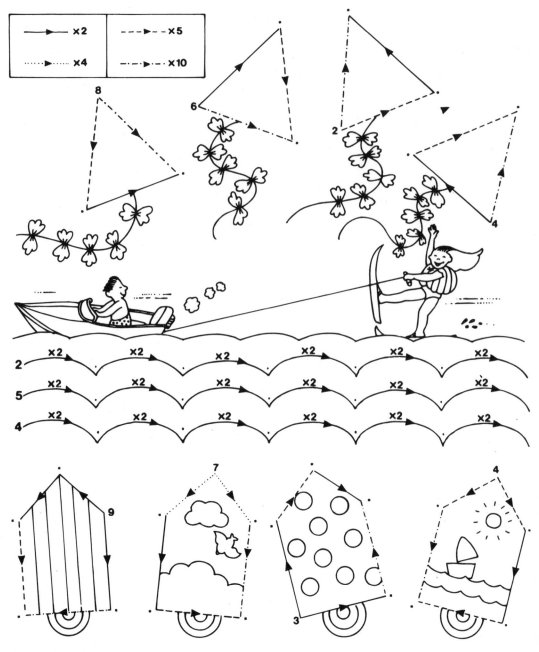

──► ×2	---► ×5	
····► ×4	─·─► ×10	

Objective: to practise multiplication.

The verb and the subject

 The subject is the person or thing *doing* the verb (action word). Can you join the right subject with the right verb to make a sentence?

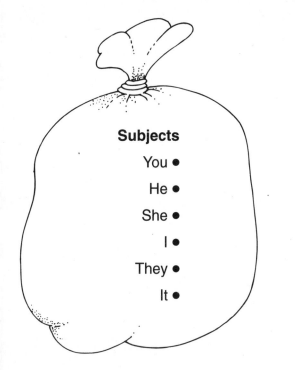

Subjects

You ●

He ●

She ●

I ●

They ●

It ●

Verbs

● **is** my aunt.

● **am** playing football.

● **are** my friend.

● **is** a hero.

● **is** too early.

● **are** going home.

 Here is a list of subjects. Complete the sentences, starting with the verb.

Your teacher ....

Tomorrow, that huge car ....

My mother and I ....

David's spectacles ....

Our house ....

I ....

You ....

The bottle of lemonade ....

Objective: to recognize subject and verb.

Gym exercises!

 The two lines which meet at the corner of a square or rectangle make a **right angle**. Which is the right angle here? Put a cross beside it.

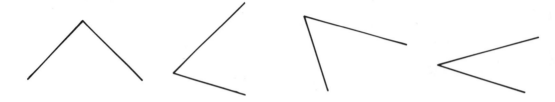

 John wants to be a gym teacher. What angles is he making with his legs in relation to the floor? Less than (<) or more than (>) a right angle? Or equal (=) to a right angle?

 Mark all the right angles in these shapes.

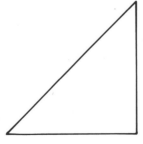

Objective: to recognize and define right angles.

Playing with letters

Unscramble the letters and write the word under each picture.

Objective: to construct words and to spell correctly.

Bobby Bear

Can you do these sums for Bobby Bear? As you finish each one, colour the patch in a different colour.

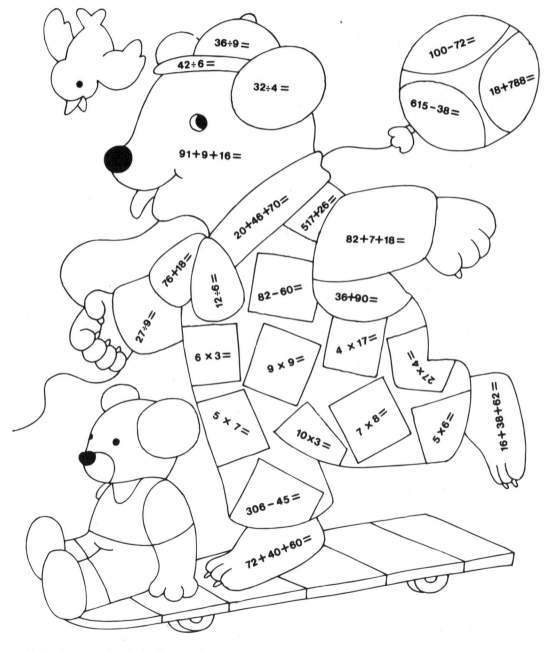

Objective: practice in the four basic maths skills.

Nouns and pronouns

A pronoun is often used instead of a noun, for example 'he' or 'she' instead of names. Copy each sentence using the pronoun 'we' instead of 'I'. You may also need to change the verb!

I must go to bed early because I am very tired.

....

I had old shoes, so I bought some new ones.

....

I am pleased because I won a bike in the competition.

....

In these sentences, replace the pronoun 'you' with the pronoun 'she'. Do not forget to check the verbs!

You spread jam on your bread.

....

On Sunday you went walking in the woods.

....

At break-time you play at marbles or hide-and-seek.

....

You put your toys in your red box.

....

Replace the pronoun 'he' with the pronoun 'they' in these sentences.

He cuts his little brother's hair.

....

He will certainly win the race next year.

....

He has driven the car to the garage for repairs.

....

Objective: concept of pronouns and use of correct verb tenses.

The telephone

How many telephone numbers can you de-code and make into a sum? Here is an example to show you how it is done.

Take the number 54 46 89.
Multiply the first number by 1, the second by 2, the third by 3 and so on. You will arrive at the following result:

(5 x 1) + (4 x 2) + (4 x 3) + (6 x 4) + (8 x 5) + (9 x 6) = ...

66 87 19 = (6 x 1) + (6 x 2) + (8 x 3) + (7 x 4) + (1 x 5) + (9 x 6) = ...

22 78 65 = (. x 1) + (. x 2) + (. x 3) + (. x 4) + (. x 5) + (. x 6) = ...

52 28 22 = ...

54 45 47 = ...

46 32 88 = ...

Now try the next lot of sums. Take care – the code has changed a little!

23 64 99 = (2 - 1) + (3 - 2) + (6 - 3) + (4 - 4) + (9 - 5) + (9 - 6) = ...

34 89 78 = ...

26 98 88 = ...

69 96 69 = ...

Objective: practice in addition, subtraction and multiplication.

Change the sentences

 Sentences can be written in the **affirmative** (doing something), in the **negative** (not doing something), or the **interrogative** (asking a question). Change these sentences, following the example:

Sophie is playing ball.
Sophie is not playing ball.
Is Sophie playing ball?

When you are hungry, you want to eat.

....

....

Nicky is hiding behind a thick bush.

....

....

Yesterday, we went to bed early.

....

....

You like to eat cake.

....

....

Objective: the concept of the affirmative, negative and interrogative.

My calendar

 Fill in the missing words with the help of the calendar.

Stacey wants to write down all her appointments.
What is the first day of the month? It is a ....
What is the last day of the month?   It is a ....

Every Tuesday and Thursday Stacey goes to music lessons.
How many times does she go in one month? ....
What are the dates of her lessons?   ....

 Now fill in your own calendar for this month. Then answer the
questions.

mon	tues	wed	thurs	fri	sat	sun

What month is it?

....

This month has .... days
with .... complete weeks.
If today were the 8th of the month, it
would be a ....
What is the date of the full moon?

....

Objective: effective use of a calendar.

Verb tenses

 Each verb has many tenses. Three tenses are shown here - the present tense, the imperfect tense (something which began in the past and is still happening, e.g. *She **had been gone** a long time.*) and future tense. Can you finish this verb table, using the right tenses?

PRESENT	IMPERFECT	FUTURE
I am leaving	Mum had been leaving	We shall be leaving
I	You had been	You
I	Anne	The people
I	Jeremy had been writing	You and Dad
I	You	We shall play
I go	The milkman	The children
I	He had been sleeping	They
I	She	The guests will eat
I know	You	You

 Now choose one of the following verbs to finish each sentence. Put the verb in the right tense!

drink, fasten, laugh, receive, draw, invite, want, have, creep

Emma .... three big glasses of water after running.

You .... the lead to your dog before going for a walk.

The caterpillars .... slowly on the blackberry leaves.

Nicholas .... six class-mates to his birthday party.

Little kittens .... very soft fur.

What a great joke! You all .... !

I .... lots of presents for Christmas.

Colin .... a tree. He .... to give it to his grandma.

Objective: correct use of verbs in different tenses.

Colouring

Colour the squares in the first grid by following the instructions.
Then reproduce the square on the right at the bottom of the page onto the grid. Write out the instructions of how you did it.

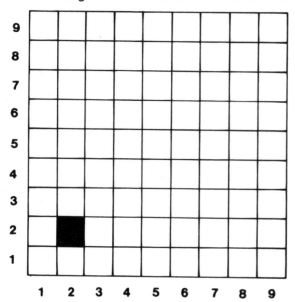

Square 2_2 has already been coloured.
Colour upwards to 5_2.
Then colour to the right as far as 5_5.
Going down, colour to 2_5.
Then going left, colour to 2_3.
The shape which appears is a

....

Now colour square 8_8. Going left, colour to 8_2. Colour square 9_2, then, going right, colour to 9_8.
The shape which appears is a

....

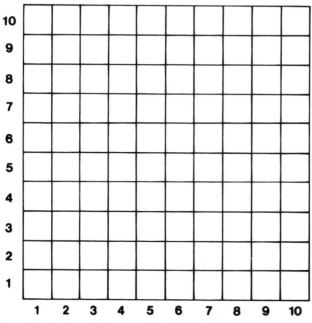

My instructions:

....

....

....

....

Objective: to develop logic and reasoning.

Words and phrases

The following words have been written back to front. Can you write each one correctly?

cincip ....

samajyp ....

srotisiv ....

elcycib ....

epocselet ....

retsnom ....

etalocohc ....

tnahpele ....

rewolf ....

ananab ....

Now write some sentences, using each of the words.

....

....

....

....

....

....

....

....

....

These words have been spelt incorrectly, even though they sound right. Can you correct each one?

feild ....

sauser ....

munny ....

kamera ....

nitting ....

labell ....

potatoe ....

pleese ....

Objective: to write sentences using given words: to improve spelling.

Let's draw!

 Time to see how well you can draw! Copy the pictures using the squares as a guide.

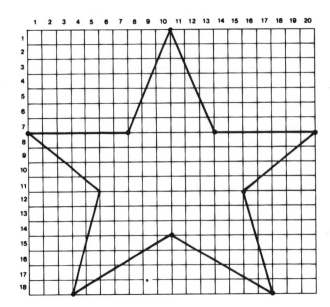
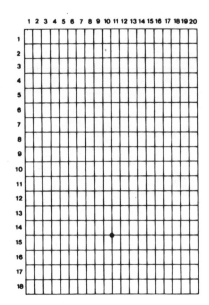

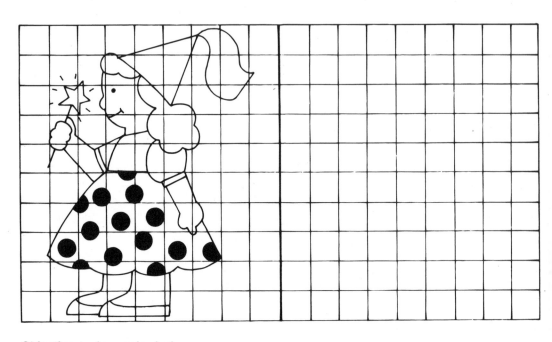

Objective: to draw, using logic.

Making sentences

 Here are some groups of short sentences. Can you change each group into a single sentence? The first one has been done for you.

I sleep in the bed.
The bed belongs to me.
I sleep in the bed which belongs to me.

I like to go walking in the woods.
The woods echo with the cries of birds.

....

....

The children are going to the beach.
The beach is covered with fine sand.

....

....

I do my homework at four o'clock.
My homework is very difficult.

....

....

David picks up the apples.
The apples have fallen from the tree.

....

....

The birds are building a nest.
The nest will be ready when they lay their eggs.

....

....

Objective: the concept of subordinate clauses.

At the grocer's shop

123 A grocer must keep his shop tidy! You can help by putting all the weights and measures in the right order, starting with the smallest amount.

½ kg, 1 kg, 100g, 10g, 3 kg : ....

2 x ½ kg, 2 x 1 kg, 2 x 100 g: ....

50 g, ¼ kg, 3 x 250 g, 75 g: ....

1 litre, 10ml, 2.5 litres, 60ml ....

45ml, 3 litres, 1.75 litres, 15ml ....

75ml, 3.5 litres, 4 litres, 34ml ....

123 How heavy is this basket of groceries? The basket itself weighs 500g. Change all the weights into kg (1kg = 1000g) and set out the sum on the basket.

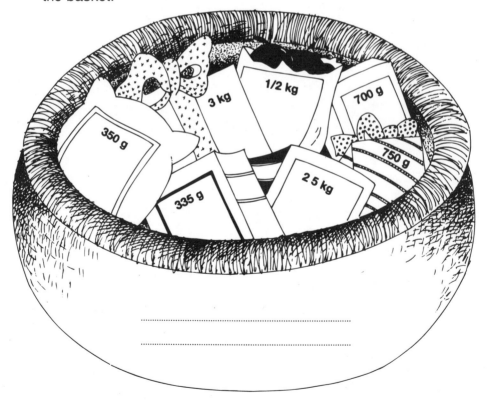

Objective: working with metric weights and measures.

Spelling exercises

Which of these words belong in the following sentences?
to - direction (*I gave the book **to** him.*) **too** - also (*He came, **too**.*)
two - 2 (*I have **two** brothers.*)

I went ... the park. Did you go ....?

How many sweets did you give ... him? One or .....?

Mark went .... the cinema. .... of his friends went .....

where - direction (***Where** is the house?*)

were - part of a verb (*They **were** out.*)

.... is the lemonade? There .... two

bottles on the table .... they on a tray?

Yes, I think they .... but .... are they now?

their - belonging to them.

there - direction (*He is over **there**.*)

.... brother is ill. He is in that hospital ....

Look at the hedgehogs over ....

.... prickles look sharp!

.... is the book that .... teacher lost.

through - direction. (*He went **through** the park.*)

threw - part of a verb (*He **threw** the ball.*)

John went .... the gate and into the park.

He could see a little boy with an ice-cream

.... the fence. The little boy .... his

ball over the fence. John went .... the gate

and fetched it for him.

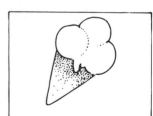

Objective: to distinguish between similar-sounding words with different meanings.

Juggling numbers!

Try these adding-up and taking-away sums! How many can you do?

100 + 200 = ...	90 + 60 = ...	150 + 60 = ...
200 + 300 = ...	50 + 20 = ...	120 + 20 = ...
700 + 200 = ...	70 + 60 = ...	420 + 70 = ...
300 + 400 = ...	40 + 30 = ...	530 + 20 = ...
500 + 200 = ...	10 + 60 = ...	720 + 90 = ...
400 + 600 = ...	80 + 30 = ...	750 − 80 = ...
100 + 300 = ...	30 + 20 = ...	680 − 80 = ...
400 + 200 = ...	20 + 90 = ...	460 − 90 = ...
200 + 500 = ...	10 + 70 = ...	320 − 70 = ...
800 + 100 = ...	80 + 10 = ...	150 − 30 = ...

600 − 300 = ...	60 − 30 = ...	160 + 810 = ...
800 − 100 = ...	50 − 10 = ...	140 + 790 = ...
900 − 700 = ...	90 − 80 = ...	530 + 180 = ...
600 − 200 = ...	40 − 20 = ...	220 + 720 = ...
400 − 300 = ...	30 − 10 = ...	390 + 270 = ...
500 − 400 = ...	90 − 50 = ...	760 − 430 = ...
700 − 400 = ...	90 − 60 = ...	840 − 280 = ...
600 − 500 = ...	70 − 50 = ...	510 − 370 = ...
500 − 100 = ...	80 − 20 = ...	620 − 280 = ...
900 − 700 = ...	70 − 40 = ...	830 − 760 = ...

Objective: practice in addition and subtraction.

Punctuation

Put the right punctuation marks in the following sentences. The first one has been done for you.

What are you doing here?

It is not hot said the fireman

Help I can see a spider

I like to walk in the rain

Look

The wolf was hiding in the woods

I think it is getting cold

Can you come with us asked David

Is that Uncle Jack's son

go away I do not want to see you here

tomorrow we shall go to the cinema

What time is it

Isnt it dirty sighs the pig

Who ate the last biscuit

Can you answer these questions?

How many full stops did you use? ....

How many commas? ....

How many exclamation marks? ....

How many question marks ? ....

How many speech marks? ....

Objective: learning to use punctuation correctly.

The birthday calendar

123 Here is a list of birthdays. Look at the first one, then write in each column the day in numbers or in letters.

| 16 February 1987 | 16. 2. 87 | 19. 3. 81 | 19 March 1981 |

11 July 1986 .... 5. 5. 87 ....

18 October 1982 .... 28.10.82 ....

19 January 1984........................ 31. 3. 86 ....

 8 August 1985 .... 4. 9. 80 ....

123 On this calendar, colour in the following dates: your birthday, your mother's birthday, your father's birthday, your friends' birthdays, your brother or sister's birthday.

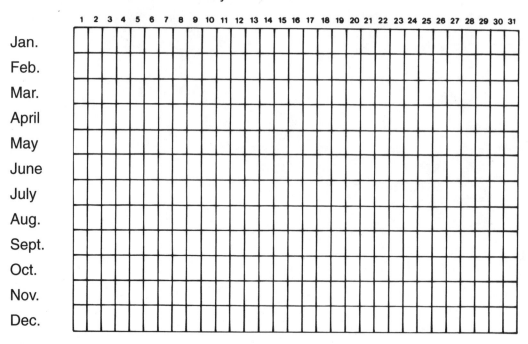

123 Complete these sentences.

The year is divided into .... months and in one year there are .... days.

When there is a Leap Year, the month of .... has 29 days.

So, in a Leap Year, there are .... days.

Objective: learning to use the calendar.

Rings and things!

Finish off the rings by writing the correct words around each one.

celery	carp	rose	daisy
apple	plum	herring	salad
beech	plaice	oak	leek
poplar	swallow	cod	birch
robin	carrot	nut	melon
primrose	sparrow	tulip	blackbird

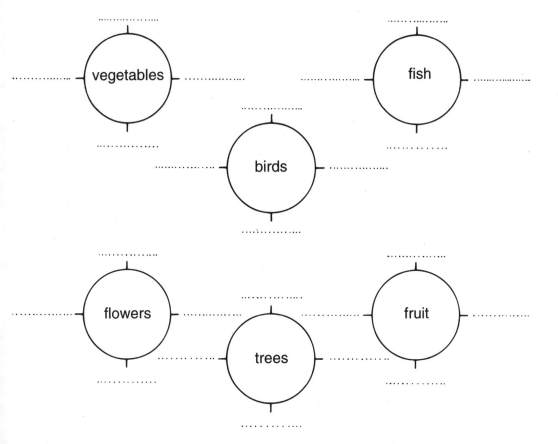

Objective: to put words into categories.

The three angles

 Draw a right angle. Then draw an angle smaller than a right angle (acute angle) and an angle bigger than a right angle (obtuse angle).

_____   _____   _____

    a right angle   a smaller angle (acute)   a larger angle (obtuse)

 Put an X in the angles which are smaller than a right angle.

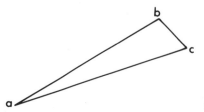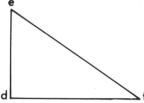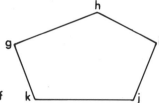

 Draw a L over each right angle.

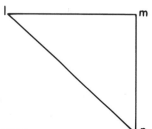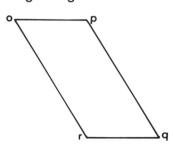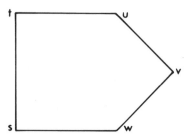

 Choose the correct sign: < (less); > (more); = (equal to).

angle a .... angle s	angle e .... angle r
angle k .... angle m	angle p .... angle d
angle b .... angle f	angle w ....angle l
angle h .... angle q	angle v .... angle l
angle t .... angle g	angle s .... angle v

Objective: concept of angles.

The animal game

Write the name of the species (type) on the dotted lines, next to each picture. Then write the name of each animal in the right place.

SPECIES	ANIMAL		
mammals	rat	butterfly	mosquito
reptiles	pike	toad	pigeon
birds	frog	mole	eagle
insects	squirrel	goldfish	fly
fish	owl	salamander	crocodile
amphibians	dog	bee	sole
	carp	sparrow	snake
	alligator	newt	turtle

Objective: to classify animal-life into species.

Opposites

 Can you complete the list of opposites?

hot	cold
dry	
good	
weak	
narrow	
quick	
small	
fat	
ill	
first	

 First write a sentence containing each of the following words, then a sentence containing the opposite of each one.

slow: 1. ....

2. ....

naughty: 1. ....

2. ....

soft: 1. ....

2. ....

tall: 1. ....

2. ....

Objective: learning the concept of opposites.

Battleships game

 Just follow the instructions and colour in the squares. You will soon see something you recognise.

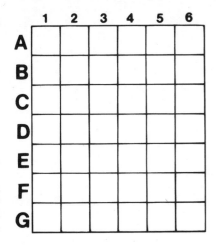

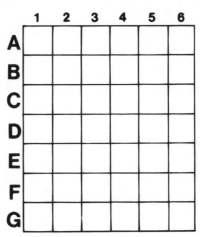

Colour squares 2B, 2C, 2D, 2E, 2F, 3D, 4D, 5B, 5C, 5D, 5E, 5F. Which letter have you drawn?

Colour the squares: 2B, 3B, 4B, 5B, 2C, 2D, 2F, 3F, 4F, 3D, 4D, 5D, 5E, 5F. Which letter have you drawn?

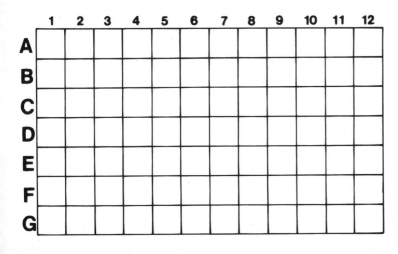

Colour in squares from 2D to 10D, from 2E to 10E, from 4B to 10B. Then colour 4C, 6C, 10C, 4F, 5F, 8F, 9F. What have you drawn?

Objective: development of logic and reasoning.

A game with shapes

These shapes have many angles. Answer the questions below, then colour in the shapes which have more than four angles.

The shapes with the following numbers .... have 5 angles. Those with the numbers .... on them have 4 angles. The shape with the number .... on it is a triangle.

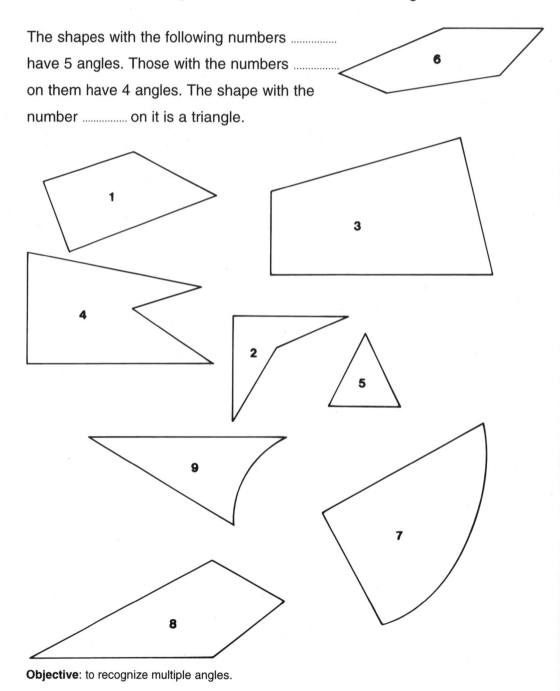

Objective: to recognize multiple angles.

Definite and indefinite articles

An article is the word before a noun. The definite article is used for one noun in particular - **the** boy, **this** house, **that** dog. The indefinite article is used for a noun in general - **a** river, **some** sweets. Join each article to the right noun.

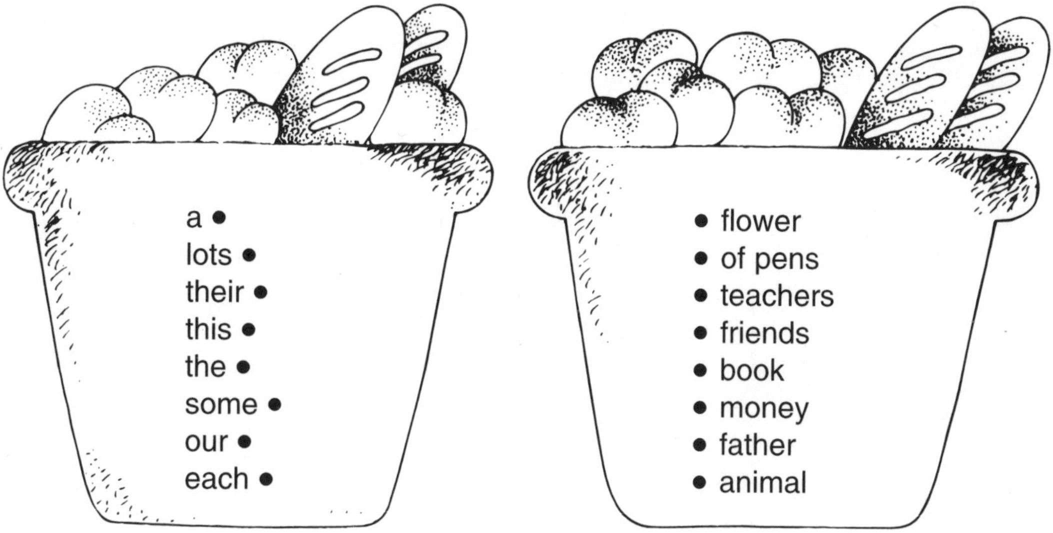

a •
lots •
their •
this •
the •
some •
our •
each •

• flower
• of pens
• teachers
• friends
• book
• money
• father
• animal

Objective: learning to use the definite and indefinite article.

Sums by stages

+− ÷× Complete each sum in turn beginning at the arrows. The number in the first square will also be the answer to the last sum.

→ = 240	+ 30 =..........	+ 60 =..........	+ 20 =..........	+ 80 =..........	− 60 =..........	− 130 =..........	− 50 =..........	+ 80 = 270

+ 90							+ 10 =..........
− 10 =..........	→ = 300	− 10 =..........	− 100 =..........	− 40 =..........	+ 30 =..........	+ 30 = 210	− 30 =..........
− 130 =..........	− 130					+ 50 =..........	− 20 =..........
− 20 =..........	+ 40 =..........					− 10 =..........	+ 50 =..........
+ 50 =..........	+ 20 =..........					− 30 =..........	− 10 =..........
− 10 =..........	+ 10 =..........					+ 70 =..........	− 70 =..........
+ 100 =..........	+ 70 =..........					− 50 =..........	− 100 =..........
	+ 90 = 290	+ 20 =..........	− 10 =..........	− 40 =..........	− 20 =..........	+ 10 = 250	

− 70 = 170	+ 10 =..........	− 30 =..........	+ 60 =..........	+ 100 =..........	− 90 =..........	− 60 =..........	+ 20 =..........	+ 130 = 230

Objective: addition and subtraction, up to 1000.

Nouns in the plural

 Look at the nouns in the left-hand column. Then write the plurals in the right-hand column. Remember, not all plurals end in the same way!

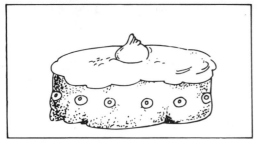

a cake	some	a horse	some........................
a sandwich	some	a mouse	some ....
a biscuit	some	a turkey	some ....
an ice cream	some	a fish	some ....
a jelly	some	a pig	some ....
a loaf	some	a goose	some ....
a sausage	some	a sheep	some ....

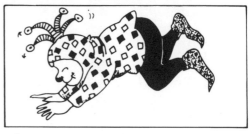

a fire	some	a jester	some........................
a field	some	a clown	some........................
a fence	some	a friend	some........................
a lorry	some	a class	some........................
a knife	some	a kiss	some........................
a berry	some	a leaf	some........................
a tomato	some	a game	some........................

Objective: to learn different forms of plural nouns.

The temperature

123 Look at these two thermometers. Fill in the correct temperatures in the sentences. Then answer the questions.

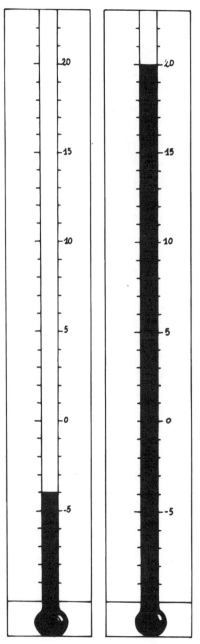

The thermometer on the left shows .... degrees below zero.

So, the temperature is .... degrees.

The thermometer on the right shows .... above zero.

So, the temperature is .... degrees.

The difference between the two thermometers is .... degrees.

How many degrees are there between:

-06° and +05°? 11 degrees.

-07° and +12°? .... degrees.

+12° and +20°? .... degrees.

+08° and -02°? .... degrees.

+04° and -07°? .... degrees.

Objective: to learn to read a thermometer and understand the concept of temperature.

At the zoo

Put the sentences in the right order to make a story. Then write the
story in the boxes. The first sentence has been written for you.

A monkey took my hat.
Then I went home.
First, I went to see the giraffes.
Yesterday I went to the zoo.
Then I went to see the monkeys.
Then he gave it to an old lady.
She gave me my hat back.
Finally, I went to see the bears.
He would not let me have it back.
I thanked her.

Yesterday, I went to the zoo.

....

....

....

....

....

....

....

....

....

Objective: to learn the process of sequencing.

A trip in a balloon

 Look at the different means of transport around the balloon. Draw a line joining each one to the right part of the balloon. The table will help you.

A = means of transport on 2 wheels = { ....}
B = means of transport on 3 wheels = { ....}
C = means of transport on 4 wheels = { ....}
D = means of transport on more than four wheels = { ....}
E = all means of transport = { ....}

Is the right group written for the right means of transport? Write a ✓ or X beside each one.

train .... D	balloon .... B	motorbike .... A	tricycle .... D
bicycle C	lorry C	pram .... A	go-cart .... A
legs .... A	car .... B	scooter .... B	

Objective: concept of group classification.

Capital letters

 Write the words which must begin with a capital letter on the balloon. Do not forget the capital letter!

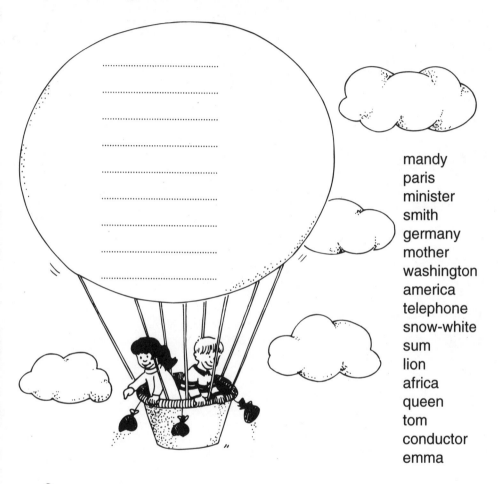

mandy
paris
minister
smith
germany
mother
washington
america
telephone
snow-white
sum
lion
africa
queen
tom
conductor
emma

 When would you use a capital letter? Write 'yes' or 'no' on each line.

After a question mark ....   To start all verbs ....

To begin ordinary nouns ....   For all proper nouns ....

After an exclamation mark ....   After a comma ....

To begin a sentence ....

Objective: to learn the correct use of capital letters.

The television programme

 Here is the list of programmes for the evening. Can you answer all the questions?

This evening
19.45 chat show
20.05 weather
       forecast
20.10 game show
20.20 film
21.45 documentary
22.30 chat show

Which programme lasts the longest? ....

How long is the chat show? ....

How long is the documentary? ....

The film lasts .... minutes longer than the documentary.

Which programme is the shortest? ....

Between 20.00 and 20.30, the viewer can see .... different programmes.

123 Draw hands on each clock face to show the time each programme begins.

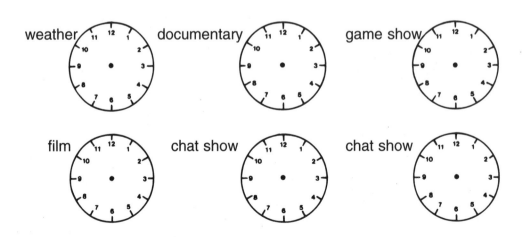

weather   documentary   game show

film   chat show   chat show

Objective: telling and measuring time.

The verb 'to be'

The verb 'to be' is quite different to all other verbs. Can you see why?

TO BE		TO PLAY	
Present Tense	Past Tense	Present Tense	Past Tense
I *am*	I *was*	I *play*	I *played*
You *are*	You *were*	You *play*	You *played*
He *is*	He *was*	He *plays*	He *played*
She *is*	She *was*	She *plays*	She *played*
It *is*	It *was*	It *plays*	It *played*
We *are*	We *were*	We *play*	We *played*
They *are*	They *were*	They *play*	They *played*

In the verb 'to be', the verb is different for each subject (I, you, he, she, it, we, they). For other verbs, it is almost the same for each subject. Try writing the verb 'to be' for each subject here.

We w.......... at the circus yesterday. The clowns w.......... so funny! I w.......... still laughing when I .... at home!

A..........you a fan of those clowns?

We w.......... on our way to school. It .... not a nice day.

'I ....glad it ....the end of the week!' I said to David. '.......... you in my football team today?' But David .... already further along the street. 'I .... sure I saw some puppies!' he cried. '..........they lost?'

'Well, we .... the only ones in the street!' I said. 'Or .... that lady driver the owner?'

'Yes, she ....!' cried David. 'Look how pleased they .... to see her!'

Objective: correct use of the verb 'to be' in present and past tense.

Gerald's money box

Which key does Gerald need to open his money box? Colour the key-tag green.

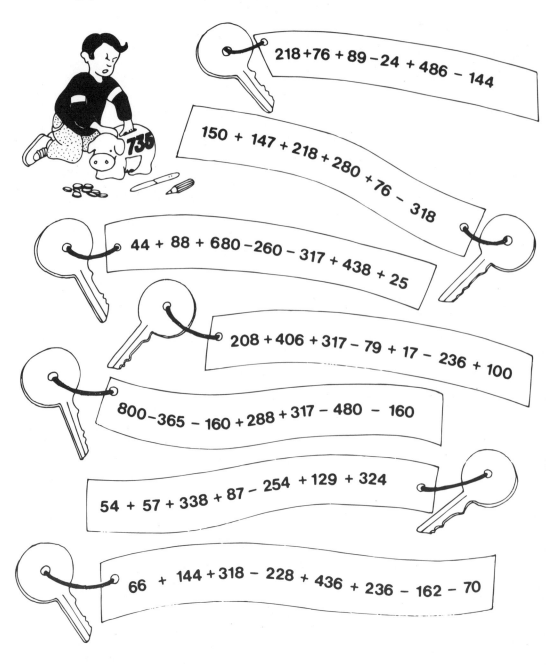

218 + 76 + 89 − 24 + 486 − 144

150 + 147 + 218 + 280 + 76 − 318

44 + 88 + 680 − 260 − 317 + 438 + 25

208 + 406 + 317 − 79 + 17 − 236 + 100

800 − 365 − 160 + 288 + 317 − 480 − 160

54 + 57 + 338 + 87 − 254 + 129 + 324

66 + 144 + 318 − 228 + 436 + 236 − 162 − 70

Objective: practice in addition and subtraction.

Crossword

 Can you do this crossword puzzle?

Clues Across

1. If you cut your finger, it may ....
1. Plural of mouse.
3. Number after seven.
3. Husband of a queen.
5. When you put on your clothes, you are ....
6. A verb which is used a lot.
7. Pilots try to make safe .... in their aircraft.
9. You can cook toast under the ....
9. Erupts from a volcano.
11. An elephant's ivory 'fangs'.
11. Another word for 'too'.

Clues Down

1. Food eaten at most meals.
1. Opposite of heavy.
3. A large bird of prey.
3. These are hammered into wood.
4. Opposite of happy.
6. A huge man in a fairy story.
8. White and sweet, spread over a Christmas or birthday cake.
8 Opposite of big.
10. Laid by a bird.
10. Looks like a mountain. Lava can sometimes erupt from it.

Objective: to develop use of language, spelling, logic and reasoning.

Sweet dreams!

Cathy cannot get to sleep, so she counts sheep! Can you do the sums and write the answers on the sides of the sheep? Colour the sheep with the same answers in the same colour.

Objective: practice in the four basic maths skills.

Place and time

 Where is Alan? Write the answer beneath each picture. The first one has been done for you.

in the car

....

....

 Take a look at these phrases. If a phrase refers to time, write it on the clock.

at 4 o'clock	in my bath	at the bank	next year
beside the king	in the castle	under the car	beneath the sea
at this moment	after dinner	before long	tomorrow lunch time

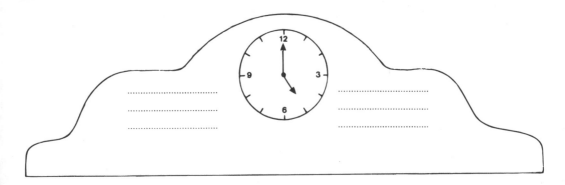

Objective: to understand the concept of place and time.

Follow the arrows!

Follow the arrows and do the sums. Write the answer in each square.

Objective: understanding the concept of multiplication.

A day at the seaside

 First, look at the pictures and the text. Then finish the story below.

'Look over there!' cries David. 'There is the sea! Run down to the beach with me!'

There is a lot of space. 'I want to fly my kite!' says Vicky.

....

....

....

....

....

....

....

....

....

....

....

....

Objective: writing a story on a given theme.

The signpost

[?] Look at this signpost. Can you answer the questions?

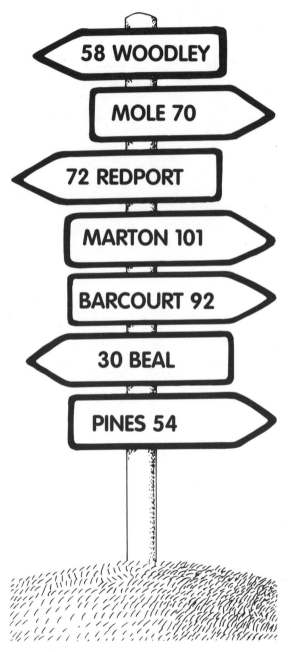

Miss Sykes comes from Woodley. She has already driven .... km. Then she is going on to Beal. She must drive another............. km. Change this distance into metres (1000 metres = 1 kilometre): .... m.

Mr. Hall is on his way to Barcourt, but his car has broken down halfway. How far has he still to go? .... km.

A brave snail is making for Pines. How far does he have to go before he gets there? .... km.

This signpost is outside a transport company which has three lorries. The driver of the first lorry is going to Mole, the second to Barcourt and the third to Pines. What is the total number of kilometres they must drive?.......km.

Their boss arrives at Redport. He has driven .... km, which is 1/ .... (*write the fraction*) of the total journey of his three drivers.

Objective: practice in the concept of distances.

In the past!

Use the verbs in the boxes to complete the sentences. Put the verbs in the past tense.

answer	play
look	take
drive	pull
build	put
finish	make

You .... hide and seek behind the house.

I .... a delicious chocolate cake.

My dad .... at the rope to bring down the branch.

Nicky and Tom .... at the magnificent blue car.

The teacher .... his chalk to write on the board.

You .... all your homework before going out to play.

The bricklayers .... a beautiful wall.

I .... lots of homework.

You .... all the questions that you were asked.

He .... a train at 100 km per hour without stopping.

We .... a great, big snowman.

You .... a lot of noise.

They .... their toys in the cupboard before taking out any more.

You .... a go-cart with your friend.

My mum and I .... at the starry sky through the window.

Objective: conjugation of different verbs in the past tense.

The fish market

How many fish are on sale on this stall? The sign shows the number of fish in each of the three tubs.

The hedgehog

 Read carefully all about the hedgehog, then answer the questions.

Some people think hedgehogs are the same as porcupines, but that is wrong. Porcupines live in hot countries, and their spikes can be up to 40cms long. A hedgehog's spikes are only a few centimetres long. These spikes protect the hedgehog from danger. When it thinks it is being attacked, the hedgehog will roll itself into a ball, with the spikes sticking out.
An adult hedgehog is about 25cms long. It eats mainly insects, but also small animals, birds' eggs, fruits and grain. In winter, the hedgehog hibernates. It rolls itself into a ball and its breathing and heart rate slow down.

Is the hedgehog the same as a porcupine? Why not? ....

....

....

What is the purpose of the hedgehog's spikes? ....

....

What does a hedgehog eat? ....

....

What changes are there in a hedgehog when it hibernates? ....

....

....

Objective: comprehension; applying given information correctly.

The sports club

 Mary plays tennis, Anne plays table tennis and Tom plays football. Answer the questions, using the numbers given for each item of sports equipment.

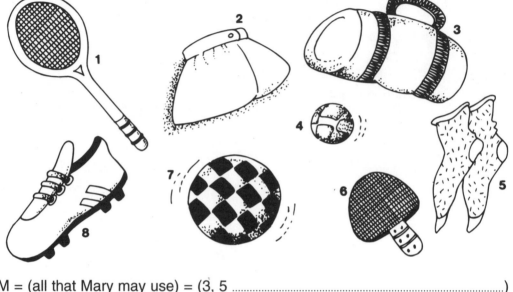

M = (all that Mary may use) = (3, 5 ....)

A = (all that Anne may use) = (3, 5 ....)

T = (   ) = (3, 5 ....)

 More than one person may need the same item. (e.g. Mary and Anne will each need a sports skirt). Write the name of each person (M = Mary, A = Anne, T = Tom) beside each item. Can you enter this information on the chart?

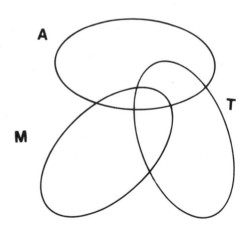

Objective: recognizing common elements of groups: converting information to a chart.

The subject group

Read the following sentences and draw the subject group in the squares.

At six o'clock, the little
birds begin to sing.

Look! John and Christine
have already arrived!

The squirrels are playing
in the big oak tree.

The strawberry tart is nicer
than the apple pie.

Now complete the sentences using a subject group of your choice.

At midnight .... made a terrible noise.

.... enjoy doing school work.

.... are eating pancakes with jam.

In the forest, ... are creeping along the ground.

In autumn, ... collect acorns.

.... are going to the seaside in August.

.... can often get lost in the jungle.

Objective: to understand the concept of a subject group.

The apple tree

Write the same number on the apples of the same size in each tree. You can check your answers by working upwards.

Change these sentences!

 Here are some sentences written in the *negative.* Each one basically says 'not' or 'no'. The *affirmative* says 'yes'. Can you change each sentence into the affirmative?

John has not gone on holiday.

John has gone on holiday.

Sarah does not want to go to school.

....

The birds are not flying to Africa this winter.

....

 Here are some sentences written in the affirmative. Change them into the negative.

He has telephoned his grandma.

He has not telephoned his grandma.

She wanted to throw the ball to her brother.

....

Deborah has planted a tree in the garden.

....

You have taken a knife to cut the bread.

....

 Here are some sentences which are exclamations. Can you change them into the affirmative?

What lovely eyes you have!   *You have lovely eyes.*

What a sweet little girl! ....

Oh, what beautiful countryside! ....

Objective: understanding the concept of the affirmative and negative.

Operation sweets!

Rosa and Mark are being naughty! Change their words into numbers to make a code. Then count up the numbers to make a total.

a b c d e f g h i j k l m n o p q r s t u v w x y z
1 2 3 4 5 6 7 8 9 10 11 12 13 14 15 16 17 18 19 20 21 22 23 24 25 26

Mark, = 13 + 1 + 18 + 11 = 43   In = ...

Mum = ...   the = ...

is = ...   cupboard! = ...

out. = ...   Let = ...

Where = ...   us = ...

are = ...   get = ...

the = ...   them = ...

sweets? = ...   down! = ...

TOTAL: ....   TOTAL: ....

Objective: logic, reasoning and 'de-coding' words into numerals.

Make sentences

 Write some sentences, using the words in the box.

birthday		fun
animals		hibernate
autumn		leaves
holidays		journey
books		book shop
smoking		health
teacher		board
Mary	hungry	bread
glass	water	salt
pillow	bed	sleep

....

....

....

....

....

....

....

....

....

Objective: to construct sentences using given words.

Series

 Can you write the correct numbers to continue the series on each line?

Objective: to develop the concept of progression.

Adjectives

 An adjective describes a noun. Write an adjective for each noun in the first column, and a noun for each adjective in the second.

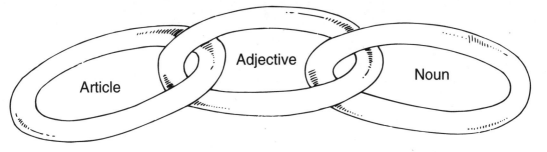

The article is either 'a' ('an' when the next word begins with a vowel, a.e.i.o.u) or 'the'.

a .... lesson	an	old...
a .... castle	the	beautiful...
a .... dog	an	ugly...
a .... child	the	naughty...
a .... journey	the	clever...
a .... camera	the	sparkling...
a .... morning	the	pretty ....
a .... friend	the	funny...
a .... pencil	an	upright ....
a .... film	an	ill...
a .... cake	an	angry ....
a .... satchel	an	icy...
a .... car	an	open ....
a .... computer	the	wooden...
a .... prize	the	crowded...
a .... game	the	horrible ....
a .... present	the	tall...

Objective: use of adjectives.

The cowboy

Join up the numbers inside the cowboy's lasso. Go in the direction of the arrows, following the instructions below.

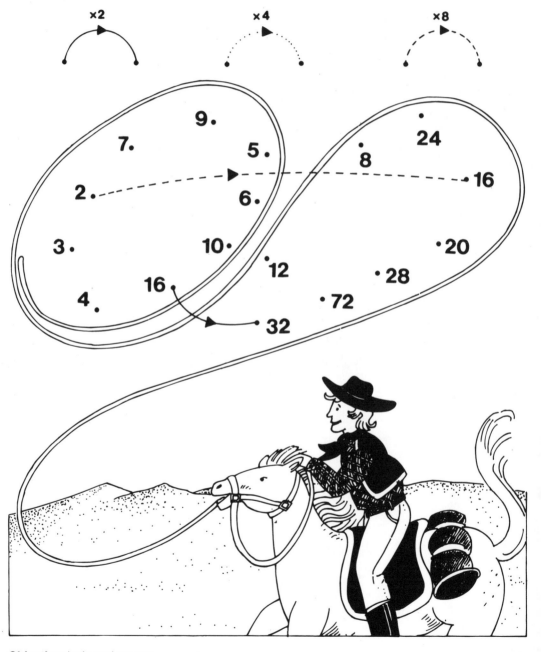

Objective: logic and reason.

Start with the subject!

 In a sentence, the **subject** is the person, the thing or the animal 'doing' *the verb* (action word). eg. **Miss Brown** *bought* a new handbag.
The clock *had stopped*. **Misty the cat** *won* first prize at the show.

Here is a list of sentences. Can you write each one so that they start with the subject? The examples below will show you how it is done.

> On top of the hill stood an old castle.
>
> **An old castle stood on top of the hill**.
>
> Yesterday we went on a picnic.
>
> **We went on a picnic yesterday.**

This morning, Mum bought some apples at the greengrocers.

....

Yesterday, I was in bed by 8 o'clock.

....

Tomorrow, I will do my homework at four o'clock.

....

'Happy Birthday!' cried the children.

....

Barking with delight, the dog ran to meet his master.

....

With a loud crash, the picture fell to the floor.

....

By four o'clock the letter had arrived.

....

Next Saturday, we are going on holiday.

Objective: to define the subject and to use correctly.

On the right side!

Draw over each straight line with a red pencil.

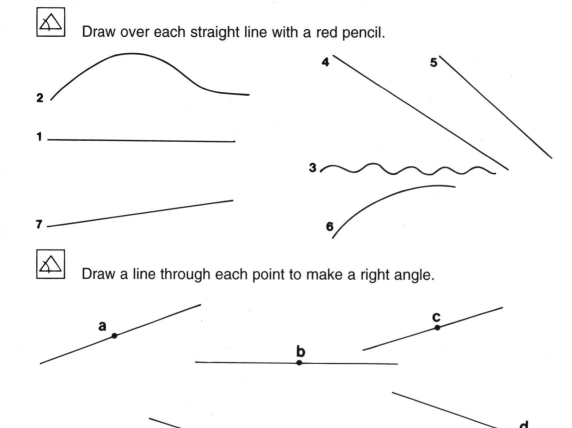

Draw a line through each point to make a right angle.

Which lines will intersect each other if you make them longer. Circle the letters.

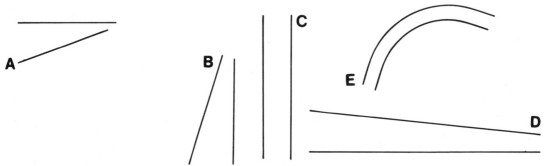

Objective: to recognize and define right angles.

Snowballs!

 Make sentences with the words in each snowball. Write them at the
bottom of the page, then put them in the right order to make a story.

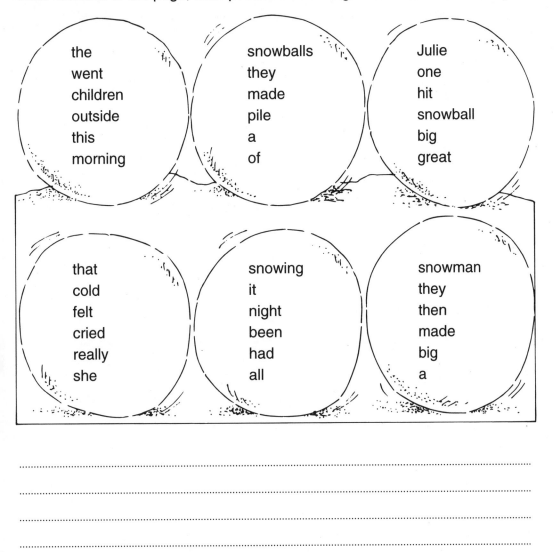

the
went
children
outside
this
morning

snowballs
they
made
pile
a
of

Julie
one
hit
snowball
big
great

that
cold
felt
cried
really
she

snowing
it
night
been
had
all

snowman
they
then
made
big
a

....

....

....

....

....

....

....

....

Objective: making sentences with given words and sequencing correctly.

Bowls

 James, Yvonne and Vince are having a bowls match. Their name is written on the ball and the jack is in the middle. Who wins the match?

Each one plays two bowls per game. Whose bowl gets nearest the jack? The first gets 3 points, the second 2 points, the third 1 point. Write the points for each player on the board.

The winner is ....

	Game 1	Game 2	Game 3
James			
Yvonne			
Vince			

Game 1

Game 2

Game 3

James .... cm
Yvonne .... cm
Vince .... cm

James .... cm
Yvonne .... cm
Vince .... cm

James .... cm
Yvonne .... cm
Vince .... cm

Objective: to measure and compare effectively.

The four seasons

 Write the correct season and words associated with it, beside the right picture.

snow	bonfires	swimming	acorns
harvest	Christmas tree	sunshine	cold
holidays	blossom	buds	lambs
chestnuts	flowers	swimsuit	ice skates

....

....

....

....

....

....

....

....

....

....

....

....

Which season do you like best?
Can you say why?

....

....

....

....

Objective: classification of words; writing independently.

Playing with dice

Play this game with your friends. Throw a dice in turn. Can you do the sum in the square where you land? If you land on a drawing, miss a turn.

start **1**	8 × 3 **2**	(6 × 5) ÷ 2 **3**	**4**
10	(6 ÷ 3) × 9 **9**	Go back to the start **8**	(7 × 8) ÷ 4 **7**

	(6 ÷ 3) × 9 **9**	Go back to the start **8**	(7 × 8) ÷ 4 **7**	6 × 2 **6**
72 − 56 **11**	Go forward two squares. **12**	(48 − 20) ÷ 7 **13**	(97 − 37) − 48 **14**	**15**
20	84 ÷ 7 **19**	Go back three squares **18**	(8 − 3) × 4 **17**	(2 × 4) × 3 **16**
(27 + 8) − 20 **21**	Have another go **22**	(6 × 4) + 1 **23**	Go back three squares. **24**	finish

Objective: practice in the four basic maths skills.

Find the words

Join each word to its description and the right picture.

saxophone	piece of curved wood which returns to the thrower
boomerang	set of questions which must be answered
computer	beautiful flower with a stem which is covered in thorns
candlestick	it is different each day, and brings us news from around the world
rose	a tool which measures temperature
newspaper	machine with an 'electronic brain'
architect	person who designs plans for houses and other buildings
questionnaire	a holder for candles
thermometer	a woodwind instrument

Objective: development of vocabulary.

The windmills

Divide the number shown at the centre of each windmill by the numbers shown underneath. Write your answers on the sails of the windmill.

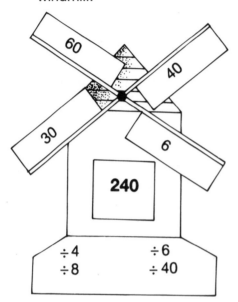

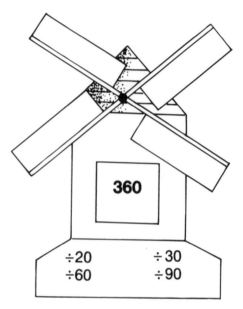

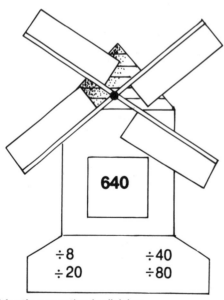

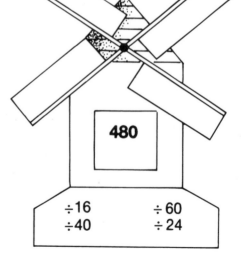

Objective: practice in division.

Crossword puzzles

 Can you solve the following crossword puzzles?

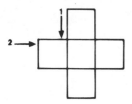

1. Catch fish in this.
2. You sleep in this.

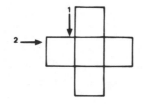

1. One more than one.
2. Bird out at night.

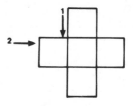

1. Opposite of good.
2. Pet animal.

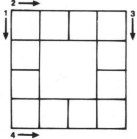

1. Every one, separately.
2. Laid by birds.
3. Small, wooden building.
4. Above the neck!

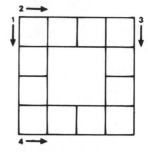

1. We get this from trees.
2. Red Riding Hood's animal.
3. Begins life as a tadpole.
4. To pull.

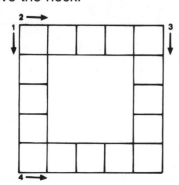

1. Chased by a cat.
2. Another name for car.
3. To stretch.
4. The name of our planet.

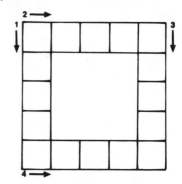

1. Slow-moving creature.
2. Opposite of large.
3. Opposite of heavy.
4. The smallest amount.

Objective: development of vocabulary and correct spelling.

Fun in the snow!

 Add the numbers together to find the total number of points on the snowman.

 The picture of the big snowman shows you the points for each part of him. Add the points for each small snowman and write the total. Then finish each drawing.

Objective: practice in addition and subtraction.

Word-play with vowels

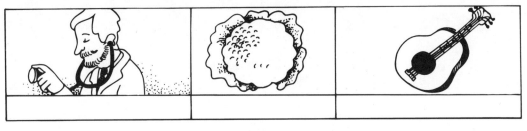

Write in the vowels (a, e, i, o, u) to complete all the words. The picture at the top of each column will give you a clue.

d . ct . r	c . . l . fl . w . r	g . . t . r
d . nt . st	p . t . t .	tr . mp . t
ch . m . st	c . rr . t	v . . l . n
gr . c . r	br . cc . l .	p . . n .
dr . v . r	c . bb . g .	tr . mb . n .
t . . ch . r	t . rn . p	s . x . ph . n .
b . k . r	p . . s	h . r p

tr . . s . rs	f . . tb . ll	. . r . pl . n .
h . t	sw . mm . ng	tr . . n
sh . rt	t . nn . s	l . rry
s . cks	b . sk . tb . ll	c . r
dr . ss	j . d .	b . . t
j . mp . r	sk . t . ng	b . cycl .
j . ck . t	cycl . ng	b . s

Objective: correct spelling and use of vowels.

A game of football

Laurence, Billy and Alan all want to score goals. None of them want to be the goalkeeper! So, they have worked out a plan. Chalk marks divide the goal into nine squares, with each square having a score. Fill in the table to find out which footballer gets the highest score.

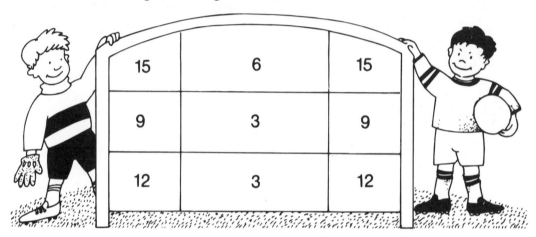

		Billy		Alan	
Laurence					
bottom left	12	top right		on the post	
middle top		middle right		over the bar	
bottom left		over the bar		top left	
over the bar		in the centre		bottom right	
total		total		total	

Who has won? ....

Objective: Reasoning and logic; practice in addition.

Shops and businesses

Here are the names of some shops and businesses. Who works there? Write the word and draw a picture.

post office

pharmacy

garage

café

hairdressing salon

dairy

beauty salon

library

Draw something you would see in these places.

bank

stables

hardware shop

butcher's shop

florist's shop

supermarket

china shop

haberdashery

Objective: to develop vocabulary.

I can tell the time!

123 Draw the hands on these clock faces to show the right time.

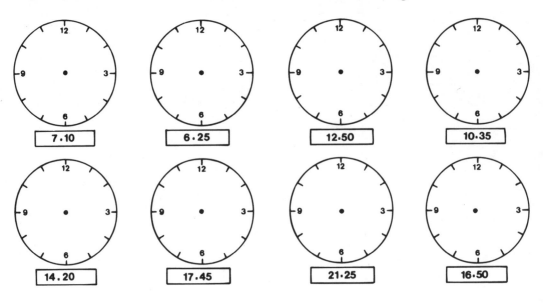

| 7.10 | 6.25 | 12.50 | 10.35 |

| 14.20 | 17.45 | 21.25 | 16.50 |

123 What time is it? Write the correct time in figures below each clock.

10.25

Objective: to tell the time to the nearest minute.

Word picture puzzles

 Can you find the answers to these picture puzzles? There is an example to show you how it is done.

 hand
b hand **g**

.... = bang

Here are a few more!

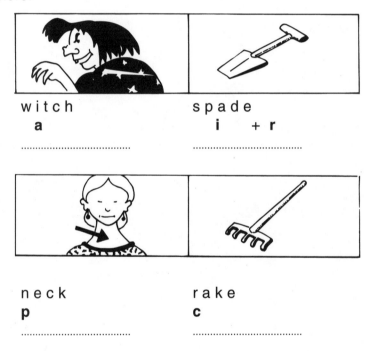

w i t c h
a

....

s p a d e
i   **+ r**

....

n e c k
p

....

r a k e
c

....

Now make up your own word picture puzzles.

....

pen   **cat**   **silk**

Objective: development of vocabulary.

The Olympic Games

 Read the following passage carefully. Then write beside each picture who is using which method of transport.

Your country is sending 145 athletes to take part in the Olympic Games. They are all travelling by air. The sports reporters are going by coach. Each of the two coaches can carry 56 people. The team managers are going by car. They travel in five cars, each car with four seats. 480 supporters are arriving by train. The Prime Minister and his wife will travel by helicopter.

How many people in total are going from your country to the Olympics? ....

How many will be travelling by road? ....

Which will be the largest group to arrive? ....

Objective: logic and reasoning.

Write a story

 Write down what is happening in each picture. These four pictures will form a story.

....

....

....

....

....

....

....

....

....

....

....

....

....

....

....

....

....

....

....

....

Objective: explaining events in writing.

Fractions

Count the black sections in each shape. Can you write this number as a fraction of the whole shape? The first one has been done for you.

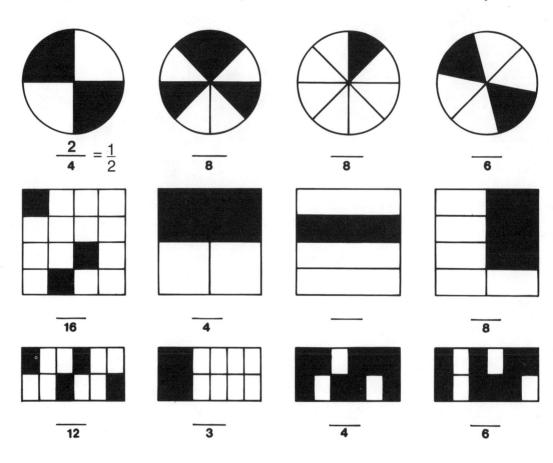

$$\frac{2}{4} = \frac{1}{2}$$ $$\frac{}{8}$$ $$\frac{}{8}$$ $$\frac{}{6}$$

$$\frac{}{16}$$ $$\frac{}{4}$$ $$\frac{}{}$$ $$\frac{}{8}$$

$$\frac{}{12}$$ $$\frac{}{3}$$ $$\frac{}{4}$$ $$\frac{}{6}$$

A fraction has been written beneath each shape. Can you colour in the correct portion of the shape?

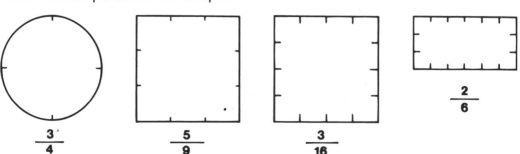

$$\frac{2}{6}$$

$$\frac{3}{4}$$ $$\frac{5}{9}$$ $$\frac{3}{16}$$

Objective: understanding and working with fractions.

End of a journey

 Write a story using the words in the box.

Train	carriage	platform	hug
station	dad	present	return

....

....

....

....

....

....

....

....

....

....

....

....

....

Can you decide on a title for your story? ....

....

Check list!
Are all the words clearly written?
Have you used the right punctuation?
Does the story make sense?
Have you used capital letters in
the right places?

Objective: sequencing; writing a story.

The slalom ski slope

 Follow the skiers on this slalom slope, and do the sums as you go!

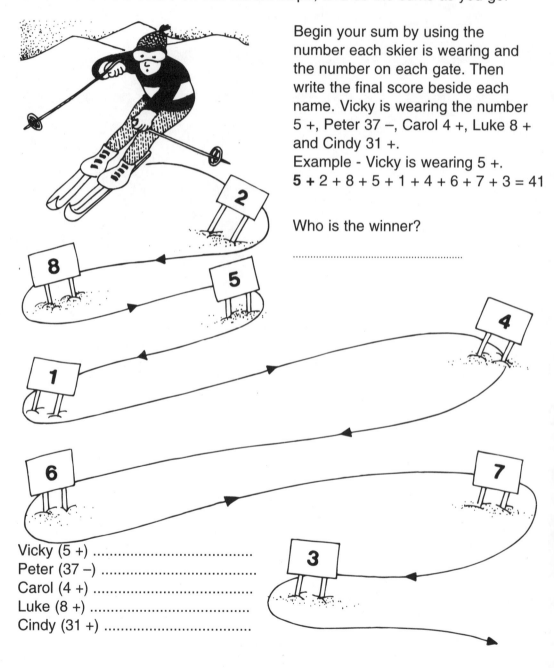

Begin your sum by using the number each skier is wearing and the number on each gate. Then write the final score beside each name. Vicky is wearing the number 5 +, Peter 37 −, Carol 4 +, Luke 8 + and Cindy 31 +.

Example - Vicky is wearing 5 +.

5 + 2 + 8 + 5 + 1 + 4 + 6 + 7 + 3 = 41

Who is the winner?

....

Vicky (5 +) ....
Peter (37 −) ....
Carol (4 +) ....
Luke (8 +) ....
Cindy (31 +) ....

Objective: to work with addition and subtraction.

Subjects and verbs

Join the subjects and the verbs which go together. Write some longer
sentences, using these phrases as a start.

They ●	● are roaring
Your sister ●	● were dancing
She ●	● was returning
The tigers ●	● has gone
Mary and Jill ●	● are blooming
Mandy ●	● is travelling
You ●	● have spent
The driver ●	● was waiting
The flowers ●	● are going
Alan and Henry ●	● is selling
The grocer ●	● have danced
He ●	● are visiting
We ●	● has played

....

....

....

....

....

....

....

....

....

....

....

....

Objective: to link subjects with appropriate verbs.

Mr. Weather Man

You are Mr. Weather Man! Your job is to show the temperature of each country on this chart by filling in each section.

France	▓▓▓▓▓											
Italy												
USA												
Egypt												
Russia												
China												
Morocco												
Spain												
	0°	5°	10°	15°	20°	25°	30°	35°	40°	45°	50°	55°

Objective: to record temperatures on a chart.

Present, imperfect or future tense

 The imperfect tense describes a verb which began in the past and is still going on. (*They **had been** friends for a long time.*)

Write the imperfect, present or future tense in each sentence. The verb is shown in the infinitive (the root or beginning of the verb).

Next Sunday, I (*to work*) .... in the garden.

I (*to be*) .... behind the door.

You (*to wash*) ....your face and (*to brush*) your teeth.

Oaks (*to be*) .... magnificent trees.

We (*to look*) .... out for traffic when crossing the road.

Yesterday evening, you all (*to dance*) .... in the dining room.

I (*to sleep*) .... soundly because I (*to be*) .... very tired.

Next winter, I (*to make*) .... a lovely snowman.

Suddenly, he (*to hear*) .... a noise.

Very soon, you (*to leave*) .... on holiday.

I (*to ask*) if Michael (*to travel*) .... by train or aeroplane.

You (*to receive*) .... a nice present for your next birthday.

Last Tuesday, Eric (*to tidy*) .... his bedroom.

Objective: conjugation of verbs in the present, imperfect and future tenses.

Paws and claws!

 Look at these pictures. Write in the number of legs for each animal. Then finish each sum.

.... legs .... legs .... legs

5 mice = ... 7 spiders = ... 4 wasps = ...

.... legs .... legs .... legs

9 crocodiles = ... 8 birds = ... 10 squirrels = ...

.... legs .... legs .... legs

3 cats = ... 6 foxes = ... 7 storks = ...

10 mice and 4 cats = (10 x 4) + (4 x 4) = 40 + 16 = 56

5 wasps and 4 birds = ...

3 foxes and 5 spiders = ...

4 storks and 5 squirrels = ...

Objective: practice in multiplication and addition.

Let's go!

 Can you answer the following questions?

The bicycle is a well-known form of transport.
Do you know any others? Write them down here!

....

....

....

....

....

....

How do you travel to school? ....

Write down all the details of your journey to school: ....

....

What do you think is the best form of transport? ....

Why? ....

....

....

Write about something which you have seen on your way to school.

....

....

....

....

....

....

....

Objective: to write complete answers to specific questions.

Hundreds, tens and units

123 Look at the first picture. The number on the sail is in hundreds (3), tens (7) and units (0). Can you do the same with the rest of the pictures?

3 hundreds
7 tens
0 units

....

....

....

....

....

....

....

....

....

Objective: to define hundreds, tens and units.

Animals and plants

 Look carefully at the words set out on this page. Can you put the other words in the box in the right places?

Mammals, fish, birds, goldfish, blackbird, animals, migratory birds, reptiles, stork, cow, swallow, snake, sparrow, non-migratory birds

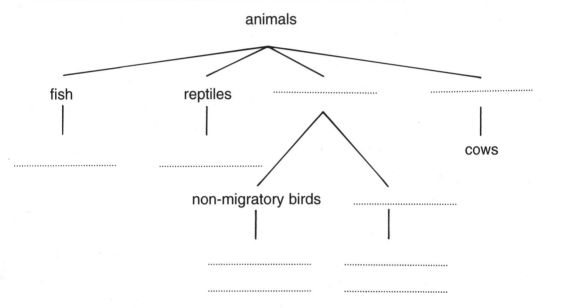

 Put the names of the fruits in the right group.

chestnut   pineapple   apricot   apple   cherry   pear
orange   lemon   redcurrant   banana   grapes

Home grown fruits ....

....

Fruits from hot countries ....

....

Objective: to classify words into groups.

Bars of chocolate!

? The four children below play monopoly with chocolate money. Read the text below carefully then fill in the chart. A small bar of chocolate = 3 pieces of chocolate, large bar = 8 pieces, giant bar = 16 pieces. To the left of the chart, you will see how much chocolate each player starts the game with. At the bottom of the page you will see how many pieces of chocolate each person has to pay out. Put crosses in the grid to show how many bars of chocolate each player has to use and how many pieces they will get back as change. eg Anne pays out 18 pieces = 1 large bar + 4 small bars. She will get 2 pieces back.

Anna

1 large bar
5 small bars

Marie

2 large bars
9 small bars

Lucy

3 giant bars
1 small bar

Jake

5 giant bars
2 small bars

	large bar	small bar	giant bar	pieces returned
	✕	✕ ✕ ✕ ✕		✕ ✕

Anna:
18 pieces
Marie:
24 pieces
Lucy:
33 pieces
Jake:
22 pieces

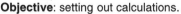

Objective: setting out calculations.

Adjectives

 Complete the sentences on this page using one of the following adjectives. You can use the same adjective more than once.

main	fat
lazy	cute
beautiful	delicious
last	green
magnificent	pleased
new	yellow

The .... pig could not get through the gate.

'How .... we look!' they said, looking at themselves in the mirror.

The mayor unveiled the .... statue.

The .... ball bounced on the .... grass.

This strawberry tart is truly ....

The .... girls do not want to do any work.

The .... cars to arrive lost their way.

The .... cups do not yet have any cracks.

'You have worked hard!' said Mum, ...

My new doll is so ....

The .... roads come together at the centre of town.

I was given some .... bracelets for my birthday.

Now it is really winter. The .... leaves have fallen from the trees.

The .... canaries are singing in their cage.

Objective: appropriate use of adjectives.

Less (<), more (>) or equal (=) ?

123 Finish off these exercises by filling in the right symbol.

38 + 9	☐	29 – 3	9 × 3 ☐	54 ÷ 2
13 + 8	☐	6 × 7	33 ÷ 3 ☐	4 ÷ 2
38 ÷ 2	☐	60 ÷ 3	53 – 10 ☐	25 × 4
54 – 5	☐	70 – 11	10 × 10 ☐	9 ÷ 3
2 × 9	☐	6 × 3	30 – 6 ☐	38 ÷ 2
3 × 20	☐	44 – 6	84 – 8 ☐	32 ÷ 2
30 – 4	☐	53 – 8	28 × 3 ☐	5 × 13
45 + 3	☐	54 – 5	4 – 2 ☐	2 × 1
63 – 7	☐	72 + 9	10 + 12 ☐	60 – 6
21 – 11	☐	3 + 7	74 – 62 ☐	28 ÷ 4
29 + 9	☐	24 – 8	58 – 43 ☐	3 – 2
25 + 9	☐	4 × 9	19 – 7 ☐	9 × 20

Objective: to learn to calculate using mathematical symbols.

Check your spelling!

Finish the sentences on this page, using the right spelling.

to or **too**

'It is .... hot to go .... school

.... day!' Tom said .... his mother.

'Can't we go .... the swimming pool?

You like swimming, ... !'

.... hot to go .... school?' said his

mum. 'And it's your swimming lesson,

.... !' Tom laughed.

His mum laughed ....

'I forgot .... check!' Tom said. 'There

is a cricket match, ...

through (direction - *He went **through** the room*) or **threw** (past tense of

throw - *She **threw** the ball*)

Lena .... the ball to her dog. 'Don't go .... the gate!'

called her dad. 'If you .... the ball on the road, it could cause an

accident!' Lena did not want to go .... the gate to the road!

Instead she and the dog played hide and seek .... the bushes.

no or **know**

Most people .... my Great Uncle Sam. There is .... happier

person in town! .... matter what may happen, he has .... time

for being miserable. 'I may have .... money,' he says, 'but I

.... that I have good friends! So there is .... need to worry!'

Great Uncle Sam is the nicest man that I ....

Objective: distinguishing between words which sound the same.

The party

 Jenny and Lucille are at a lovely party! Work out how much this present has cost!

360 + 7
= ....

130 + 96
= ....

480 − 99
= ....

total:
....

No party is complete without a special cake! Do the sums, then join the total to the right slice of the cake.

(30 + 2) − (6 + 3) = 32 − 9

(38 − 6) + (22 + 1) = ...

(62 + 3) − (61 − 30) = ...

(84 + 2) − (40 + 3) = ...

(22 + 2) − (11 + 1) = ...

(13 + 2) − (7 + 2) = ...

(60 − 3) + (2 + 2) = ...

(60 + 10) − (34 + 30) = ...

(10 + 2) − (4 + 1) = ...

(72 + 2) − (30 + 4) = ...

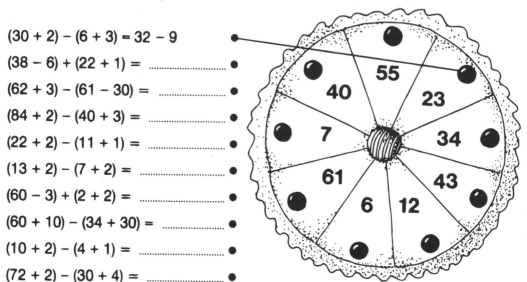

55
40
23
7
34
61
43
6 12

Objective: practice in addition and subtraction.

The human body

 Here is a skeleton. Can you name each part of the body?

brain
foot
neck
knee
hip
shoulder
elbow
ankle
hand
wrist

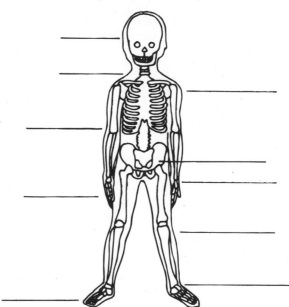

_____

_____

_____

_____

_____

_____

_____

_____

_____

 Complete the following sentences.

I think with my ....   I bite with my ....

I look with my ....   I walk with my ....

I taste with my ....   I hold with my ....

I hear with my ....   I breathe with my ....

Put these words in alphabetical order.

memory, brain, stomach, virus, eyebrow, thigh

....

intestines, blood, eyelash, muscle, heart, bone, toe

....

Objective: to learn vocabulary relating to the human body.

The beautiful princess

Do the sums, then colour in according to the answers which you get!
30 = green 96 = yellow 12 = blue 60 = brown 84 = red

Objective: practice in multiplication.

Two stories

 Colour in the same colour, those phrases which belong to the same story.

There was a storm yesterday.	The lights changed to amber.
The clouds blew across the sky.	His dad put the brakes on.
The car stopped.	'What weather!' thinks Alan.
'I'll drive one day!' said Alan.	There came a loud crack.
A branch fell on the hen-house.	'Where will you go?' asked Dad.
The hens began to cackle.	'Germany, Italy and Switzerland!'
'But I do not have a licence yet!'	Alan ran outside to see.
'That will come,' said Dad.	He pulls off the branch.
Then the hens were happy.	'You will be eighteen next year!'
'Just be patient!'	'Eighteen!' sighed Alan.
Alan went back into the house.	His clothes were all wet.

 Can you think of a title for each story?

Title for the first story: ....

Title for the second story: ....

Objective: putting sentences in the correct sequence.

The archery target

Add up the score for each player and write it down beneath each target.

John .... points

Mark .... points

Peter .... points

Martin .... points

Ranking

1st	
2nd	
3rd	
4th	
5th	

Paul .... points

Objective: practice in addition.

Surfaces which turn

These shapes can turn in two directions – clockwise or anti-clockwise. Complete the blank shapes, using the first example as a guide.

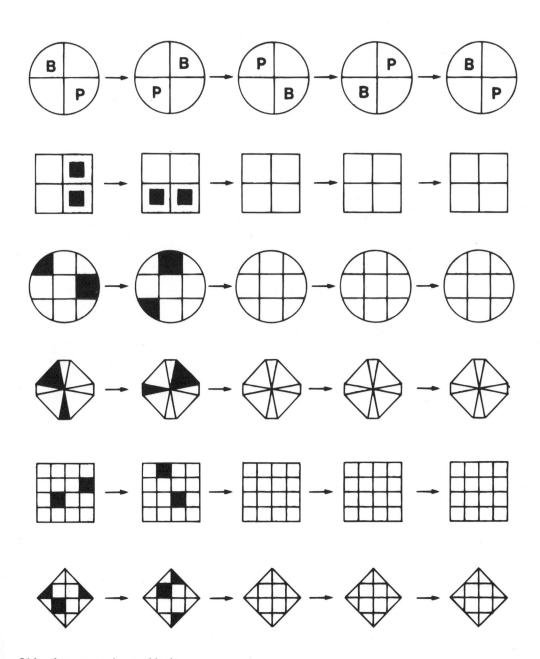

The skating mystery

 Join up the words in alphabetical order to follow the path of the ice skater.

album •

table •

nuts •

nice •

tasty •

face •

motor •

old •

sure •

savings •

alphabet •

oil •

lump •

terror •

fussy •

file •

safe •

bun •

park •

zero •

queen •

eggtea •

orange •

zebra •

lake •

ice •

violin •

each •

judo •

vat •

kayak •

burn •

yoghurt •

island •

Objective: to learn to list words alphabetically.

Word ladders

 Complete the ladders by following the instructions carefully. Use the example as a guide.

Write a noun on each rung. Each word on the first ladder must begin with the last letter of the word before. On the second ladder, write the noun in the plural. On the third ladder write an adjective which describes it.

NOUN	PLURAL	ADJECTIVE
....	....	....
....	....	....
....	....	....
....	....	....
....	....	....
....	....	....
....	....	....
....	....	....
gate	....	....
drawing	drawings	colourful
toad	toads	big

Objective: understanding use of language and vocabulary.

The swimming gala

? Can you fill in the empty spaces in this report?

Lucy, Alison, Jo and Fiona are each taking part in four swimming events –
the 200 metres, 400 metres, 600 and 800 metres. Each girl will swim a total
of .... metres or .... kilometres.
Together, they will swim .... kilometres.
The 400 metres and 800 metres relay races will take place tomorrow. Each
swimmer will swim .... metres in the 400 metres and ....
metres in the 800 metres. They will take it in turns to swim the same
distance. By the end of the day, they will each have swum ....
metres. What is the total distance of these two races?

How many 50 metre lengths do they swim in the following races:

200 m .... lengths   600 m .... lengths

400 m .... lengths (all 4 of them) 400 m .... lengths (each of them)

800 m .... lengths (all 4 of them) 800 m .... lengths (each of them)

Now, the competition has begun. When Alison gets to the end of the pool
after swimming one length, she is 10 metres ahead of Lucy. Lucy is 15 metres
in front of Jo, but Fiona has a 30 metre lead over Jo. So, Fiona has a lead of
.... metres over Alison and .... metres over Lucy.

Objective: mathematical calculation in respect of distance.

Additions

Write the following numbers in different ways using addition only.
Follow the example.

25
20 + 5
12 + 13
3 + 22
14 + 11
1 + 24

44

13

56

89

9

32

45

77

Objective: using different number combinations to get the same answer.

The road

 Look at these two tables. The line stands for 'equal to'.
(e.g. 0.48 kilometres = 480 metres). Draw lines between the distances which are the same.

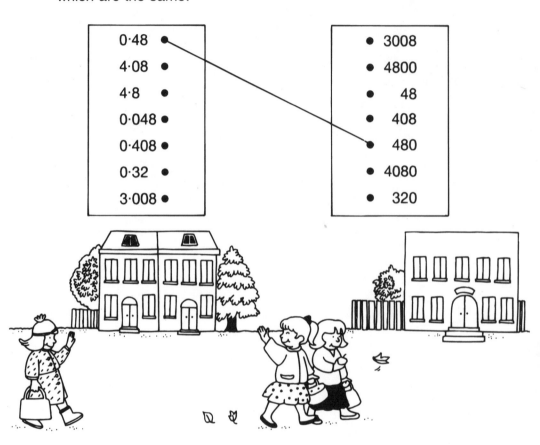

0·48			3008
4·08			4800
4·8			48
0·048			408
0·408			480
0·32			4080
3·008			320

? Can you solve this puzzle?

road	ABC	BCD	BC
length	880 m	1060 m	300 m

What is the length of road ABCD?

....

Objective: to learn to measure length.

Words in an apple

 Here is a list of words. Can you put the words which have the same ending into the right apple?

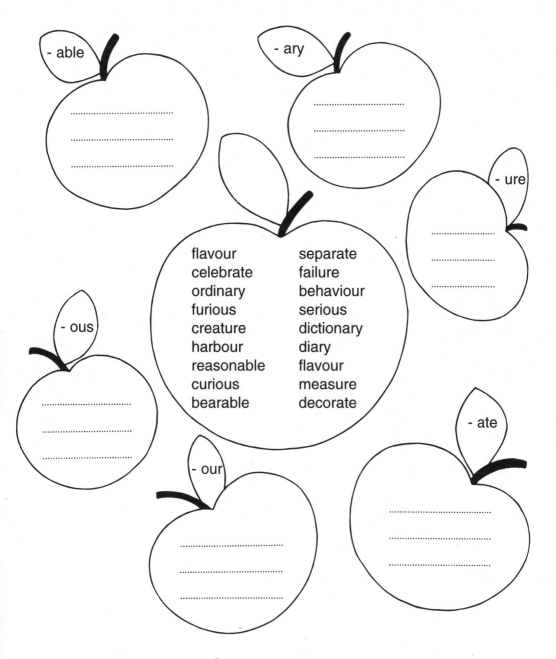

- able

- ary

- ure

- ous

flavour   separate
celebrate   failure
ordinary   behaviour
furious   serious
creature   dictionary
harbour   diary
reasonable   flavour
curious   measure
bearable   decorate

- our

- ate

Objective: to recognize common word-endings.

It's on the lorry!

This driver uses take-away sums to keep check on his load. Can you break down the second number each time, as he has done? The first two have been done for you.

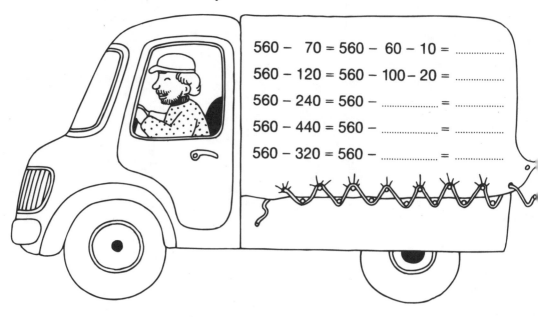

560 − 70 = 560 − 60 − 10 = ...
560 − 120 = 560 − 100 − 20 = ...
560 − 240 = 560 − .... = ...
560 − 440 = 560 − .... = ...
560 − 320 = 560 − .... = ...

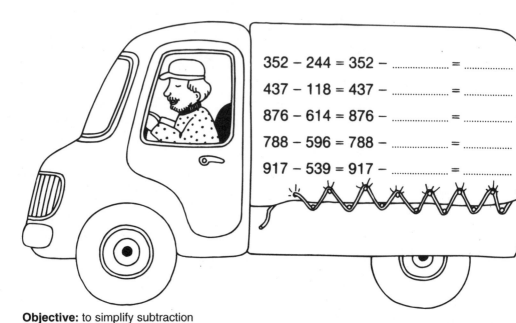

352 − 244 = 352 − .... = ...
437 − 118 = 437 − .... = ...
876 − 614 = 876 − .... = ...
788 − 596 = 788 − .... = ...
917 − 539 = 917 − .... = ...

Objective: to simplify subtraction

Singulars and plurals

 Here is a list of nouns (names of things) in the plural (more than one).
Can you write each one in the singular underneath the right picture?

nails
rings
bowls
balls
fans
windows
heads
tyres

....

....

....

 Now put these singular nouns in the plural.

mouse	goose	game	knife
house	boy	school	poppy
leaf	baby	storm	lolly
tree	box	sky	car

....

....

....

....

Objective: to define and to recognize different forms of plural nouns.

Fun and games!

 Here is a list of equipment used in different sports. Unscramble the letters, write each word, then draw a line to join it with the correct sport.

uec	....	archery
ictsk	....	golf
luckeshoctt	....	cricket
dapled	....	croquet
letlam	....	badminton
takerc	....	canoeing
bulc	....	billiards
tab	....	hockey
gettar	....	tennis

 Can you find twelve toys in this wordsearch puzzle? Look for - TEDDY BEAR, SKATEBOARD, KITE, TRAIN SET, JIGSAW, CRAYONS, DOLL, TOP, PUPPET, PIGGY BANK, YO-YO, TRICYCLE

P	S	C	K	T	C	C	G	O	B
I	K	I	T	E	R	E	R	B	A
G	A	T	O	P	A	O	A	E	T
G	T	E	D	D	Y	B	E	A	R
Y	E	Y	O	Y	O	T	K	J	A
B	B	R	L	A	N	L	E	S	I
A	O	L	L	Y	S	I	Y	O	N
N	A	I	J	I	G	S	A	W	S
K	R	T	R	I	C	Y	C	L	E
Y	D	J	S	P	U	P	P	E	T

Objective: to develop and improve spelling and vocabulary.

The circus

Can you think how all these sentences could end? They must all be about the circus! The first one in each group has been completed for you.

The conjuror takes a rabbit out of the hat.

The conjuror takes .... out of the hat.

The conjuror takes .... out of the hat.

The conjuror takes .... out of the hat.

The conjuror takes .... out of the hat.

The juggler juggles balls.

The juggler juggles ....

The juggler juggles ....

The juggler juggles ....

The juggler juggles ....

The clown trips over a bucket.

The clown trips over a ....

The clown trips over a ....

The clown trips over a ....

The clown trips over a ....

The ringmaster trains the elephant.

The ringmaster trains the ....

The ringmaster trains the ....

The ringmaster trains the ....

The ringmaster trains the ....

Objective: completing a sentence following a given verb.

Fractions

Complete these fractions. The first one has been done for you.

$$\frac{1}{4} + \frac{3}{4} = \frac{4}{4} \quad 1$$

$$\frac{1}{3} + \text{—} = \frac{\ }{3} \quad 1$$

$$\frac{1}{7} + \text{—} = \frac{\ }{7} \quad 1$$

$$\frac{1}{10} + \text{—} = \frac{\ }{10} \quad 1$$

$$\frac{1}{8} + \text{—} = \frac{\ }{8} \quad 1$$

$$\frac{1}{5} + \text{—} = \frac{\ }{5} \text{ ou } 1$$

Fill in the correct signs < meaning less than, > meaning greater than or =.

Objective: working with fractions.

The infinitive

 The infinitive is the root or start of a verb e.g. to dance, to sing, to shout etc. Can you sort out these sentences, putting each infinitive verb into the past tense?

huge creatures / In prehistoric times / the earth (to roam) ....

....

(to live) .... / Prehistoric man / for centuries / in caves.

....

The first / (to eat) .... / plants / mammals.

....

 Now put the following verbs into the present tense, following the example.

I went   I go....................................   he made..

I bought ....   I wanted...

he was..   they hid ....

you were..   you sought ....

we sang..   she chose ....

they danced..   we liked ....

Objective: to recognize verb tenses and to construct sentences.

The filling station

The metric system is measured in tens, hundreds and thousands. You can easily tell each measurement by the way it begins. milli- = 1 thousandth; centi- = 1 hundredth; and deci- = 1 tenth. Can you finish the litre table?

litre	dl	cl	ml
1	10	20	1000
2	20	200	
5			
0·5	5		
1·5	15		

0·25 litre = ... cl/ .... ml

0·75 litre = ... cl/ .... ml

1 litre = ... dl/ cl

0·50 litre = ... dl/ .... ml

Can you answer this question?

How many motorbikes with a 4 litre tank can the pump fill?

....

Objective: to understand and convert units of metric capacity.

Sylvie's dream

Sylvie is day-dreaming again! Can you put all her dream words into pairs?

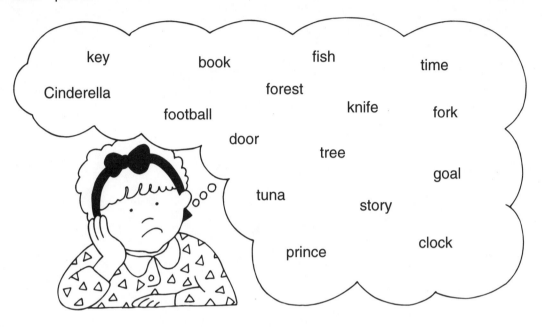

key   book   fish   time

Cinderella   forest

football   knife   fork

door   tree

goal

tuna   story

prince   clock

the key and the door

.... and ....

.... and ....

.... and ....

.... and ....

.... and ....

.... and ....

.... and ....

Now choose a few of the words and make up some funny sentences.

....

....

....

Objective: to practise word association and writing sentences.

Find the answers!

Write in the answers to each of the sums on the wallpaper!

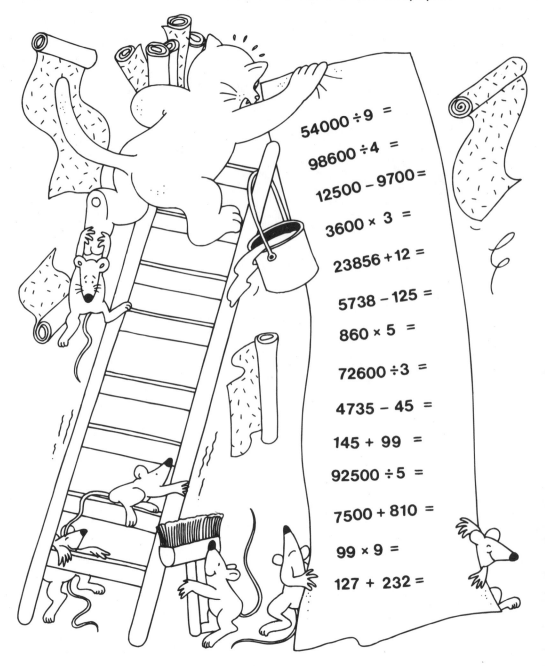

54000 ÷ 9 =

98600 ÷ 4 =

12500 – 9700 =

3600 × 3 =

23856 + 12 =

5738 – 125 =

860 × 5 =

72600 ÷ 3 =

4735 – 45 =

145 + 99 =

92500 ÷ 5 =

7500 + 810 =

99 × 9 =

127 + 232 =

Objective: practice in the four basic maths skills.

Tom gets up!

Contractions are shorter ways of saying or writing words which go together. In this story, Tom uses the following contractions.

Can you see the apostrophe (') in each of Tom's sentences? The apostrophe takes the place of a missing letter. - I'm = I am, You're = You are
Write the contraction for each of these sentences. Don't forget the apostrophe!

She is going to school.

She's going to school.

I am hoping for the best.

....

You are late!

....

It is all right!

....

We are just coming!

....

He will give you a ticket.

....

Do not be naughty!

....

Why cannot we go?

....

Objective: to recognize contractions and the significance of the apostrophe.

Mirror images

 Can you write the words and letters as reflections in a mirror? The first two have been done for you.

BEAR
_____
BEⱯꓭ

CAT
_____

LINE
_____

315
_____
3Ↄ2

268
_____

400
_____

 Complete each pattern.

Objective: creative thinking and co-ordination.

Treasure trove!

What are all these things made of? Write each one under the correct heading.

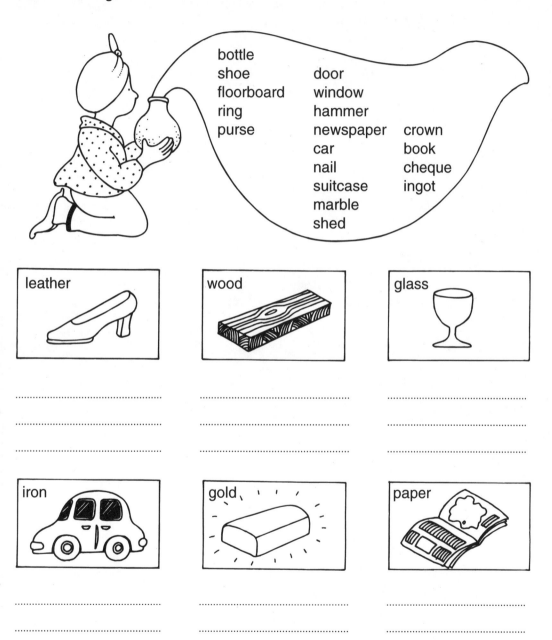

bottle
shoe
floorboard   door
ring   window
purse   hammer
               newspaper   crown
               car   book
               nail   cheque
               suitcase   ingot
               marble
               shed

leather

wood

glass

....

....

....

....

....

....

....

....

....

iron

gold

paper

....

....

....

....

....

....

....

....

....

Objective: to classify objects according to material.

Camping

 Measure the length of each line.

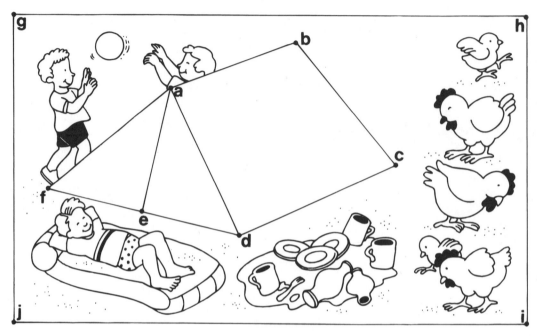

line ab = ...cm   line hi = ...cm

line bc = ...cm   line da = ...cm

line cd = ...cm   line ae = ...cm

line de ....cm   line fd = ...cm

line ef ....cm   line ij = ...cm

line af ....cm   line gj = ...cm

? Now try this puzzle.

Measure the line gh. It is .... cm long. To make an enclosure for the hens, draw a downward line 4cm to the left of h. How many enclosures could you make within the whole camping area?

.... enclosures.

Objective: practice in measuring and creative thinking.

In the past

 Complete all the sentences in this story using the past tense.

It .... spring time. Carol and Paul .... walking along

with their cat, Maxie, when suddenly the sky .... covered with

big, grey clouds. The sun .... Luckily Carol .... her nice,

new umbrella. But Maxie .... very unhappy! He ....

soaked to the skin, because there .... not enough room for him

under the umbrella! How Carol and Paul .... , all the way home.

 Finish off these verb tables, writing the infinitive, and the present, past and future tenses.

INFINITIVE	PRESENT	PAST	FUTURE
to go	I go	I went	I shall go
....	you see	....	....
....	....	He drew	....
....	....	....	they will be

Objective: to learn different verb tenses.

Draw a pattern!

 All these shapes can move round, both clockwise and anti-clockwise. Can you finish each line, following the pattern?

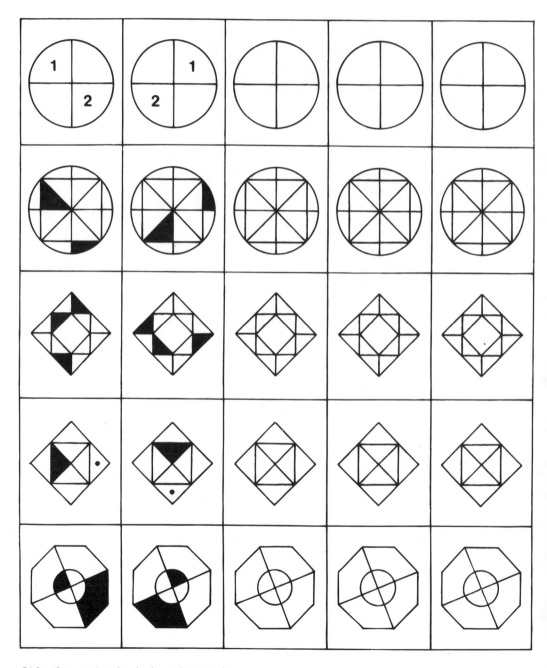

Objective: to develop logic and reasoning.

The family tree

 Here is Ray's family tree. Write the name of each member of his family, and their relationship to each other (brother, sister, etc.)

My parents have three children: Lucy, Julie and Ray.
My mother's name is Irene and my father's name is Alan.
John is my uncle. He lives in New York.
My grandma, Marie, has two sons.
The name of my mother's father is Arnold.
I have a grandfather whose name is Leonard.
My grandmother's name is Alice.
Guy is my mother's brother.

Objective: to learn the lines of parentage and family relations.

Filling the milk crates!

123 Try answering all the questions below.

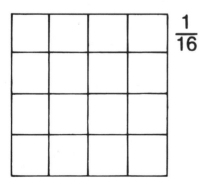

Each bottle holds 1 litre of milk.
When the crate is full it contains
.... litres. But now there are
only .... litres in it.
This means
the crate is — full.
So the crate is — empty.
8 bottles fill — the crate.

123 Fill the sections of the crate with the number of bottles shown as a fraction.

$\frac{2}{4}$

$\frac{4}{4}$

$\frac{1}{16}$

$\frac{2}{8}$

Objective: to recognize fractions expressed as numerals.

Flower centres

Each flower centre has a prefix (word beginning) in it. Colour the petals which have part of a verb which the prefix begins (re-joice, con-sider). List the remaining words below. These are all nouns (names of things)

....

....

....

Objective: to develop vocabulary and recognize verbs.

Word-Finder

 Can you find ten words, all with the ending *ous* in this word-search puzzle. Here are a few clues.

something very large	e n . . .
something or someone well-known	1 . . . . .
a person in a temper is	f u . . . . .
a beautiful sight is ....to see	m a r . . . .
full of mystery!	m y . . . . i . . .
a brave person is	c o . r . . e . . .
someone who shares things is	g e n . . . . .
hating someone for what they have is	j . . l . . .
something plain to be seen	o b . . . . .
a nosey person is always	c . r i . . .

J	J	C	O	U	S	A	E	R	M
E	E	U	B	Y	M	O	N	F	Y
M	A	R	V	E	L	L	O	U	S
A	L	I	I	O	U	F	R	R	T
F	O	O	O	O	Y	A	M	T	E
M	U	U	U	S	T	M	O	S	R
G	S	S	S	R	O	O	U	S	I
G	E	N	E	R	O	U	S	M	O
F	U	R	I	O	U	S	M	Y	U
C	O	U	R	A	G	E	O	U	S

Objective: development of vocabulary and correct spelling.

Word ladders

 Fill in the ladders by writing these words in alphabetical order.

singer	elbow	greengage	koala
gloves	elder	simple	kiosk
emperor	kangaroo	giraffe	ginger
single	slipper	sink	elastic
grass	kitten	elephant	keeper

Objective: to put words into alphabetical order.

In prison

Each prisoner has a number. First, multiply this number by 0.01, then divide the same number by 10. The example shows you how this is done.

<u>X 0·01</u>

$18\ 760 \times 0·01 = 187\ 6$

$13\ 420 \times 0·01 =$ ....

$6\ 860 \times 0·01 =$ ....

$2\ 490 \times 0·01 =$ ....

$1\ 860 \times 0·01 =$ ....

$999 \times 0·01 =$ ....

$818 \times 0·01 =$ ....

$540 \times 0·01 =$ ....

<u>÷10</u>

$18\ 760 \div 10 = 1\ 876$

$13\ 420 \div 10 =$ ....

$6\ 860 \div 10 =$ ....

$2\ 490 \div 10 =$ ....

$1\ 860 \div 10 =$ ....

$999 \div 10 =$ ....

$818 \div 10 =$ ....

$540 \div 10 =$ ....

Objective: to multiply and divide in decimals.

Annie and adverbs

An adverb describes the way a verb is done e.g. *He ran **quickly**. The dog barked **loudly.*** Underline all the verbs in this passage. Then circle the adverbs.

Annie is properly dressed for her riding lesson! She wears riding breeches, boots and a riding hat to protect her head. Annie enjoys riding enormously. To make a horse walk slowly, then canter, then trot smoothly takes a lot of patience. She has certainly learned a lot at the riding school where she goes regularly for her lessons. She knows that horses must be treated kindly, patiently and with understanding. She also knows precisely what the difference is between race horses and horses which are show-jumpers. Race horses are strenuously trained to run smoothly as well as rapidly. Those who take part in hurdles races or steeplechases are also trained to jump strongly and without fear. Show-jumpers are generally trained in a ring where obstacles have been carefully set up. With their riders sitting firmly in the saddle, each horse must clear obtacles cleanly and within a time limit. Annie frequently dreams of the great riding schools of the world, such as the Vienna and the Lippizzaner. She also dreams that one day everyone will surely know her name as a great rider.

Score .... verbs underlined

How many infinitive verbs? ....

How many verbs written in the present tense? ....

How many verbs written in the future tense? ....

How many adverbs? ....

Objective: to define and recognize verbs and adverbs.

Summer flowers!

Can you do all the sums on these flowers? The answer each time will be the number shown in the middle of the flower.

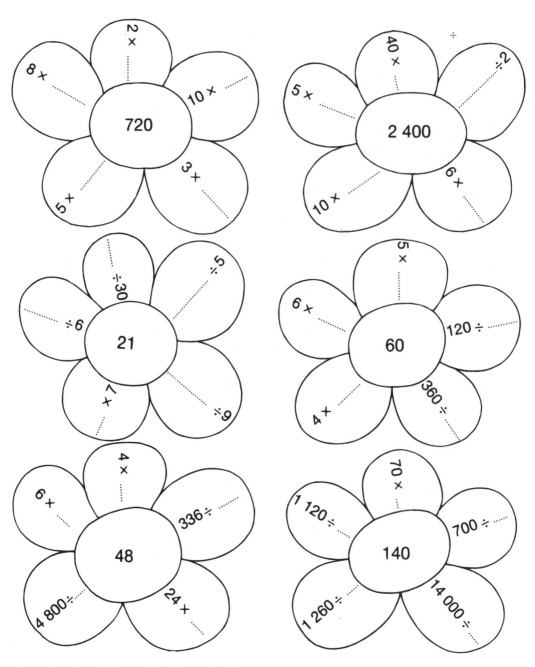

Objective: Practice in multiplication and division.

Proverbs

Proverbs are sayings which express things in a special way. Here, Colin is in the bath, thinking. Can you help him join up a proverb to what it means in everyday language?

He is reaching for the moon.

His head is in the clouds.

Sunshine always follows the rain.

The son takes after his father.

Like father, like son.

He is absent-minded.

He is dreaming.

People are happy when worry is over.

Objective: to understand the meaning of proverbs.

In class

 Write the answers to each sum on the boards at the bottom.

3·4 + 2·7 =

0·4 + 0·7 =

0·6 + 0·8 =

1·7 + 2·2 =

2·4 + 1·8 =

5·2 + 3·3 =

```
  3·4
+ 2·7
-----
  6·1
```

Objective: to add decimal numbers.

Word endings!

Angela needs some help with her spelling! Can you help, by crossing out the wrong endings for each word?

| the valu | ible | able | ring | | a music | le | | al | voice |

the valu   ible   able   ring   a music   le   al   voice

a delicious flav   our   iour   the invis   able   ible   man

some good inform   ation ition   some horr   able   ible   things

such naughty behav   our   iour   a great compet   ation   ition

an annoying nuis   ance   ence   a sci   ance   ence   lesson

a kind, little brown   ie   y   a ripe strawberr   ie   y

Presid   ent   ant   of the USA   an important docum   ent   ant

a danger   ious   ous   road   a spac   ious   ous   room

a famous act   or   er   a smart sold   ier   er

my favourite teach   er   or   a dishonest th ief   eaf

he smiled happ   ly   ily   she ran quick   ily   ly

Objective: to recognize different word endings; to improve spelling.

Tell the time!

Look at the clock. Can you write the hours in roman numerals?

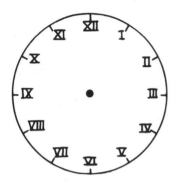

1 = ...	7 = ...
2 = ...	8 = ...
3 = ...	9 = ...
4 = ...	10 = ...
5 = ...	11 = ...
6 = ...	12 = ...

Finish off these three clock faces.

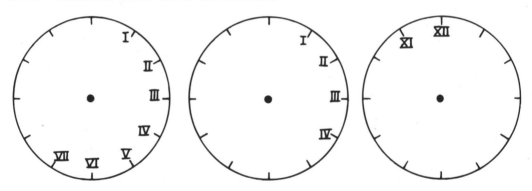

Complete these clock faces using roman numerals. Then draw the hands to show the time written beneath each clock face.

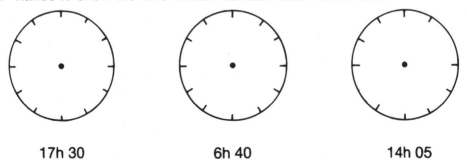

17h 30   6h 40   14h 05

Objective: to learn roman numerals.

Cherry-picking time!

These pictures tell a story. Can you write down each part of the story, underneath each picture?

....

....

....

....

....

....

....

....

....

....

....

....

....

....

....

....

Objective: to learn to write a story.

Hoist the flag!

Can you do all the sums written on the flag?

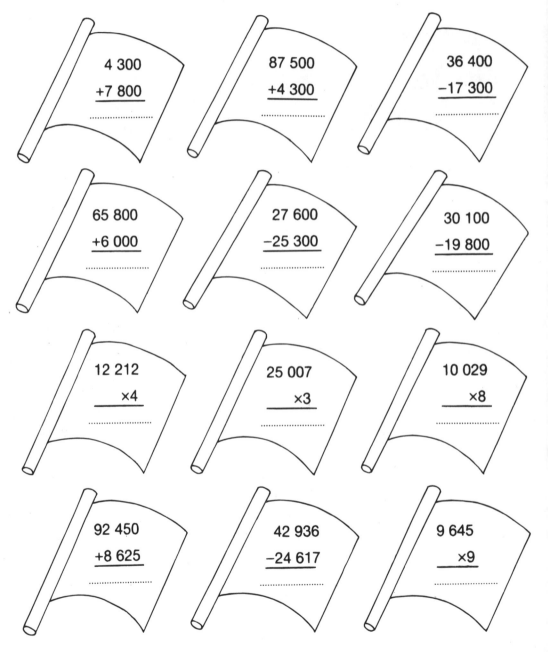

4 300 +7 800	87 500 +4 300	36 400 −17 300
65 800 +6 000	27 600 −25 300	30 100 −19 800
12 212 ×4	25 007 ×3	10 029 ×8
92 450 +8 625	42 936 −24 617	9 645 ×9

Objective: practice in the four basic maths skills.

Lots of fruit!

Here is a list of fruits. Do you know how each one grows? There are five headings to help you. See if you can write four fruits under each heading.

AS A PLANT

....

....

....

....

ON A TREE

....

....

....

....

ON A BUSH

....

.. ..

....

....

IN TROPICAL COUNTRIES

....

....

....

....

DRIED FRUITS

....

....

....

....

tomato, prune, strawberry, apple, melon, pear, pineapple, plum, banana, currant, cherry, blackberry, coconut, redcurrant, orange, blackcurrant, raisin, gooseberry, sultana, pumpkin.

Objective: classification in groups, development of vocabulary.

Off on a journey

? Read through each part of this story. Then see if you can solve each problem.

Last year, during the Christmas holidays, we went to Switzerland. We spent 6 hours travelling 1200 km on one train, which means this train went at a speed of .... km per hour. If the journey had lasted 8 hours, the speed would have been .... km per hour.

Then we caught the train to Geneva. The train left at 2 o'clock and arrived at 4 o'clock. During the journey the train stopped for half an hour. The distance covered was 135 km. So the train went at a speed of .... km per hour.

In Switzerland we went on a 6-day hike. In all, we walked for 35 hours, going up to the top of one mountain, then down and up to the top of another. We went at a speed of 5 km per hour. So the distance covered on each mountain must have been .... km.

Objective: to calculate time, speed and distance.

Who are they?

 Look at the picture. Can you make up something about these two ladies? See if you can by answering the questions.

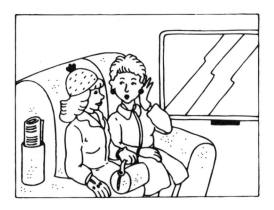

Who are these two ladies? ....

....

Where are they? ....

....

Which of the two is the kindest lady? Why? ....

....

The first is married. Can you describe her husband? ....

....

What time is it? ....

....

What was the second lady doing one hour ago? ....

....

They begin to speak. What do they talk about? ....

....

The first one gets off. Where is she going? ....

....

Objective: to write an essay along structured lines.

The hang-glider

Colour the hang-glider according to the instructions below.

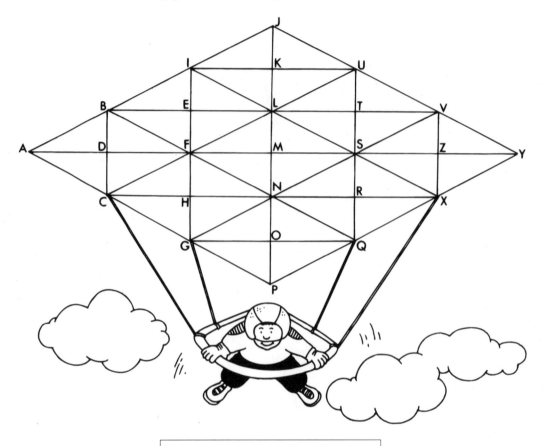

Colour four rectangles blue.
Colour eight triangles red.
Colour one diamond green.

Now use the letters to form three more rectangles, three diamonds and three triangles. The first one is done for you each time.

rectangle: BLNC,
triangle: QNG,
diamond: QNGP,

Objective: to recognize geometrical shapes.

When, where or how?

 Below there are some parts of sentences. Can you put these in the right column - when, where, or how?

'Where' indicates place.
'When' indicates time.
'How' indicates manner.

now, sadly, tonight, near the stream, in the kitchen, happily, here, during the morning, Tuesday, laughing, very quickly.

WHERE?	WHEN?	HOW?
....	....	very quickly
....	....	....
....	....	....
....	....	....

 Give a short answer to these questions.

How are you getting on at school? Very well.

What time do you get up?   ....

When are you next on holiday?   ....

How does a tortoise move along?   ....

Where do birds lay their eggs?   ....

Objective: to understand the concept of time, place and manner.

The cake

Finish the sums on this page, starting with the bottom cake layer and moving up until you reach the top.

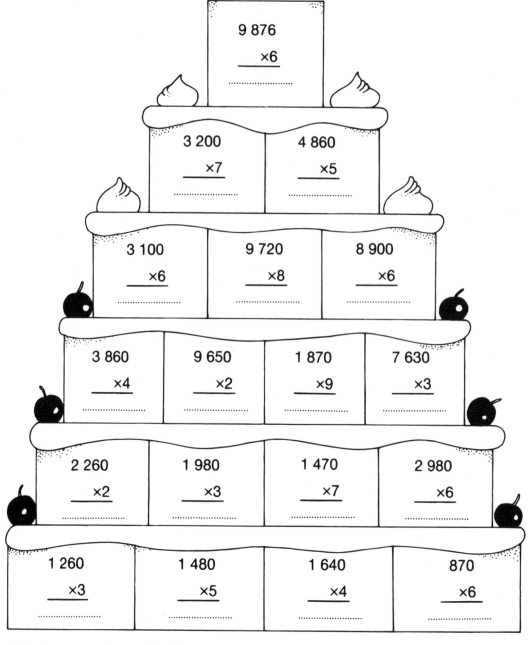

$$
\begin{array}{r}
9\,876 \\
\times 6 \\
\hline
\end{array}
$$

$$
\begin{array}{r}
3\,200 \\
\times 7 \\
\hline
\end{array}
\qquad
\begin{array}{r}
4\,860 \\
\times 5 \\
\hline
\end{array}
$$

$$
\begin{array}{r}
3\,100 \\
\times 6 \\
\hline
\end{array}
\qquad
\begin{array}{r}
9\,720 \\
\times 8 \\
\hline
\end{array}
\qquad
\begin{array}{r}
8\,900 \\
\times 6 \\
\hline
\end{array}
$$

$$
\begin{array}{r}
3\,860 \\
\times 4 \\
\hline
\end{array}
\quad
\begin{array}{r}
9\,650 \\
\times 2 \\
\hline
\end{array}
\quad
\begin{array}{r}
1\,870 \\
\times 9 \\
\hline
\end{array}
\quad
\begin{array}{r}
7\,630 \\
\times 3 \\
\hline
\end{array}
$$

$$
\begin{array}{r}
2\,260 \\
\times 2 \\
\hline
\end{array}
\quad
\begin{array}{r}
1\,980 \\
\times 3 \\
\hline
\end{array}
\quad
\begin{array}{r}
1\,470 \\
\times 7 \\
\hline
\end{array}
\quad
\begin{array}{r}
2\,980 \\
\times 6 \\
\hline
\end{array}
$$

$$
\begin{array}{r}
1\,260 \\
\times 3 \\
\hline
\end{array}
\quad
\begin{array}{r}
1\,480 \\
\times 5 \\
\hline
\end{array}
\quad
\begin{array}{r}
1\,640 \\
\times 4 \\
\hline
\end{array}
\quad
\begin{array}{r}
870 \\
\times 6 \\
\hline
\end{array}
$$

Objective: to practise multiplication.

So many suns!

 Join up the first part of each word to the sun which contains the correct ending. You can use a dictionary to help you.

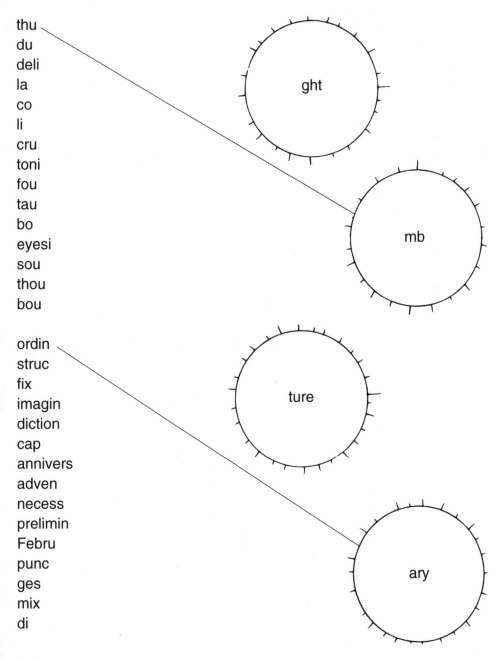

thu
du
deli
la
co
li
cru
toni
fou
tau
bo
eyesi
sou
thou
bou

ght

mb

ordin
struc
fix
imagin
diction
cap
annivers
adven
necess
prelimin
Febru
punc
ges
mix
di

ture

ary

Objective: to recognize word-endings and improve spelling.

The first division!

Can you do these sums? The first one has been done to help you.

$$\begin{array}{r} 1220 \\ 2\overline{)\,2440} \\ 04 \\ 04 \\ 00 \end{array}$$

$5\overline{)\,3420}$

$9\overline{)\,3105}$

$4\overline{)\,4840}$

$6\overline{)\,9240}$

$4\overline{)\,7120}$

$9\overline{)\,5310}$

$5\overline{)\,2840}$

$4\overline{)\,1560}$

Objective: to improve skills in division.

A holiday for the birds

 Tell the story of the birds on their holiday trip. Their conversation will help you.

'Anyone coming swimming with me?' asked the starling.
'All right!' said the chaffinch. 'Let's go swimming in the ocean!'
'We could go around the coast of Spain!' added the blackbird.
'I'm hungry!' chirped the sparrow. 'I could eat spaghetti from Italy, cheese from Switzerland and sausage from Germany, with chocolates from Belgium to finish!'
'Let's go now!' cried the starling.
'We'll have a wonderful time!' the birds cried together.

The birds gathered on a telegraph wire, talking. ....

....

....

....

They came to a restaurant in Rome. ....

....

....

....

....

....

....

.... How they enjoyed their journey!

Objective: building on a basic narrative.

Put into groups

 Draw the things which go together in three separate groups.

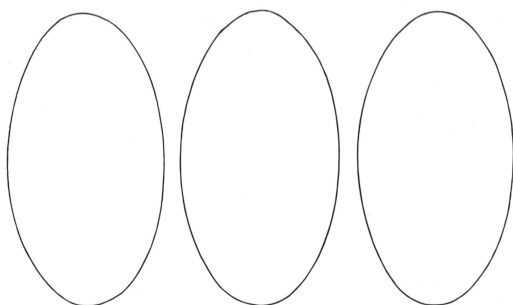

Objective: to group together objects with a common element.

Word play

Which words do you find if you follow the arrows? Write each word on the dotted lines beneath the shapes.

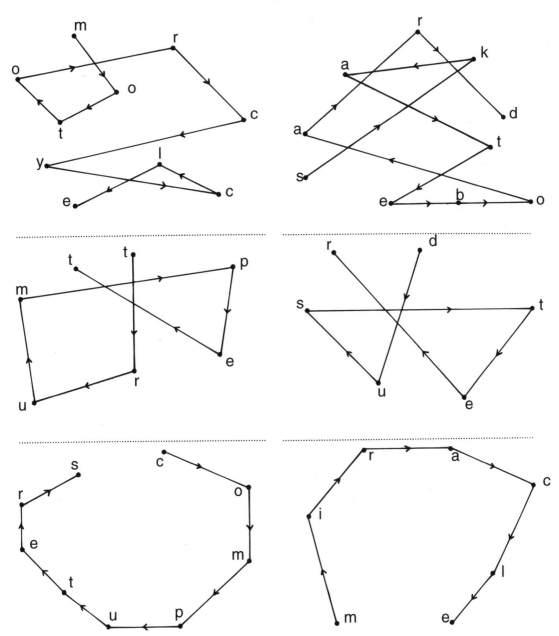

....

....

....

Objective: creative word play.

Off on holiday!

? Beth is going on holiday to a foreign country. Can you help her work out the prices of the things that she buys?

3 200 × 3

I think this coat costs more than .... ,

because 3 x 3000 = ... and it costs less

than .... because 3 x 4000 = ...

It costs: (3 x 3000) + (3 x 200) = 9600.

4 320 × 2

I think this suit costs more than .... ,

because .... X .... = ...

and it costs less than .... because

.... X .... = ...

It costs: ....

![bicycle]

1 700 × 3

I think this bicycle costs more than .... ,

because .... X .... = ...

and it costs less than .... because

.... X .... = ...

It costs: ....

![computer]

8 500 × 6

I think this computer costs more than .... ,

because .... X .... = ...

and it costs less than .... because

.... X .... = ...

It costs: ....

Objective: learning to evaluate and to multiply.

Verbal tenses and their infinitive

 Insert the infinitive (the root, or beginning) of each verb. The first one has been done for you.

Yesterday, I bought a colouring book.

On birthdays, I like (*to buy*) .... presents.

Yesterday, I sat on the see-saw.

Sometimes, I like .... on my bed.

I took my dog for a walk.

I like .... a shower.

I wrote a letter to my friend Tom.

I must learn .... in French.

At the party, I drank a lot of lemonade.

Sometimes I like .... milk.

Now I am eating some bread.

Next I'd like .... some cake.

Now, we have finished the lesson.

We'd like it .... a lot sooner.

I gave a bone to my dog.

Then I decided .... him a drink.

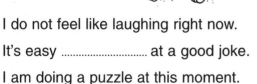

I do not feel like laughing right now.

It's easy .... at a good joke.

I am doing a puzzle at this moment.

Soon I am going .... my homework.

Objective: to recognize the infinitve of verbs from different tenses.

At the seaside

 Can you complete these series of numbers? Write your answers on the pictures.

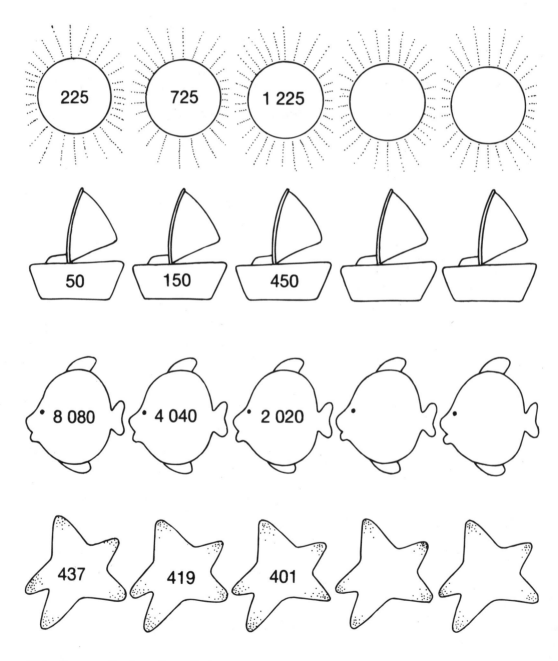

Objective: practice in mathematical sequences.

Be a poet!

Have you ever tried being a poet? Just use your imagination to write a few sentences in rhyme! We have given you an example.

If I were a cat, I would chase a big rat.

If I were a song, I would ....

If I were a star, I would ....

If I were a mouse, I would ....

Write all the words which come into your mind when you see the three words below.

sunshine ....

friend ....

butterfly ....

Can you think of words to make a funny rhyme? Read the example.

The sparrow pecks at a barrow.

.... pecks at ....

.... pecks at ....

The mouse nibbled at the house

.... nibbled at ....

.... nibbled at ....

The hare jumped over the bear.

.... jumped over ....

.... jumped over ....

Objective: to introduce rhyme.

Going up and coming down

Do the sums and write your answers down each time.

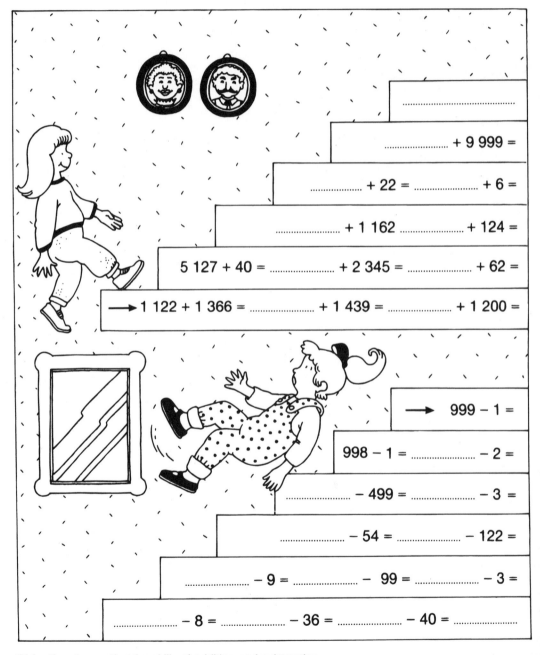

....

.... + 9 999 =

.... + 22 = ... + 6 =

.... + 1 162 .... + 124 =

5 127 + 40 = ... + 2 345 = ... + 62 =

→ 1 122 + 1 366 = ... + 1 439 = ... + 1 200 =

→ 999 − 1 =

998 − 1 = ... − 2 =

.... − 499 = ... − 3 =

.... − 54 = ... − 122 =

.... − 9 = ... − 99 = ... − 3 =

.... − 8 = ... − 36 = ... − 40 = ...

Objective: to practise the skills of addition and subtraction.

Words which sound the same!

Choose the right word for each sentence and write it in the correct place.

pear	I bought a new .... of shoes.	pair
pear	I picked a .... from the tree.	pair
heal	My broken arm has begun to	heel
heal	The athlete had a blister on her	heel
whole	The .... room was filled with boxes.	hole
whole	He fell down a .... in the road.	hole
tale	Cinderella is the title of a fairy .	tail
tale	The cat caught her .... in the door.	tail
pail	The farmer filled the .... with water.	pale
pail	The boy turned quite .... with shock.	pale
knew	My mother bought me a .... jumper.	new
knew	I .... the jumper would be too big.	new
know	You .... the person I am talking about.	no
know	I have .... money to spend.	no

Objective: to recognize and to spell homonyms correctly.

Going to the circus!

John, Ann, Katie and Tom are going to the circus. How far do they have to walk? Measure each distance in millimetres. Which one has furthest to go?

Objective: to measure to the nearest millimetre.

Geraldine's cat

 There are some mistakes in this description of Geraldine's cat. Can you write each line out correctly?

Tiggy, Geraldine's cat, is expect kittens. She is become fat and heavy,

....

and she just want to sit by the fire. Geraldine canott give her anything

....

extra to eat, becos the vet has say Tiggy must not became any biggest.

....

When her cat are about to give birth, Geraldine get a big baskett ready

....

and put it in a corner. Tiggy have five kittens. She do not want anyone

....

come near them at first! She hiss and put out her claws. The littal kittens

....

soon begin to play with Tiggys ears, and about five days later they

....

begins to get out and about like grown-up catts.

....

Objective: to recognize and correct errors in grammar and spelling.

The Olympic Games

See if you can do the division sums on this page. The example will show you the easiest way to do them!

2 400 ÷2   (2 000 ÷2) + (400 ÷2)   = ...

8 600 ÷4   .... + ... = ...

9 600 ÷3   .... + ... = ...

3 900 ÷3   .... + ... = ...

6 300 ÷2   .... + ... = ...

1 200 ÷2   .... + ... = ...

22 200 ÷4   (20 000÷4) + (2 000÷4) + (200÷4) = ...

36 600 ÷3   ....

12 400 ÷4   ....

46 800 ÷2   ....

99 900 ÷3   ....

86 400 ÷2   ....

360 900 ÷3   (300 000 ÷3) + (60 000 ÷3) + (900÷3) = ...

840 000 ÷2   ....

969 000 ÷3   ....

160 000 ÷4   ....

224 000 ÷2   ....

550 000 ÷5   ....

Objective: to learn how to simplify division.

Opposites

Join each word to its opposite.

rich ●	● never	up ●	● town
above ●	● old	small ●	● untidy
always ●	● off	country ●	● without
tall ●	● poor	with ●	● ugly
war ●	● below	beautiful ●	● old
right ●	● wrong	tidy ●	● dirty
new ●	● peace	young ●	● large
on ●	● short	clean ●	● down

 Join up the words which have similar meanings. Then write a third word to finish each group.

rude	beam	gr . .
select	sob	w . . p
academy	shake	qu . v . r
smile	afire	fl . . . . g
tremble	pick	ch . . . .
cry	uncouth	v . . g . r
burning	force	p . w . .
strength	school	c . . . . g e

Objective: to recognize antonyms and synonyms.

Shopping list

 Hannah and Jamie like playing at shops, using their own toy money. Can you fill in the spaces?

ITEM	UNIT PRICE	QUANTITY	TOTAL
pencils	10	3	....
books	90	....	270
note pads	....	2	90
pens	300	2	....
roses	....	7	245
freesias	200	9	....
carnations	10	....	150
tulips	15	3	....
cauliflowers	....	5	100
lettuces	20	9	....
cabbage	40	....	80
broccoli	42	2	....
biscuits	399	....	1 197
loaves	47	3	....
cakes	....	20	100
sweets	7	12	....

Objective: to calculate unit, total and quantity price.

Musical instruments

Underline or circle the words which are *not* musical instruments.
These words will form a message.

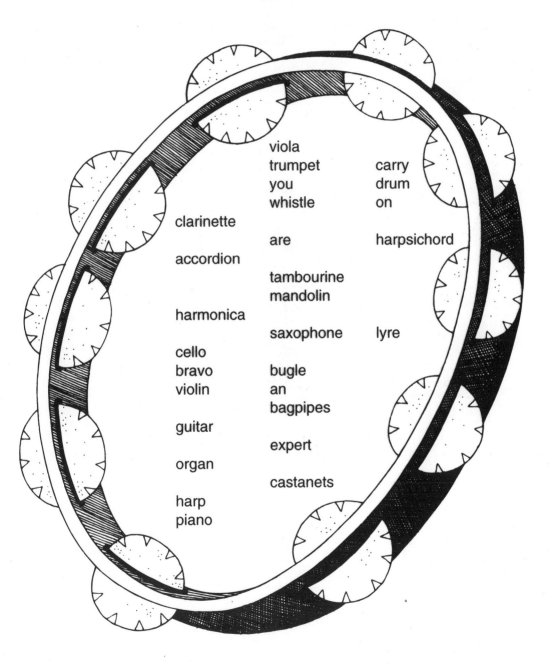

viola
trumpet   carry
you   drum
whistle   on

clarinette

             are   harpsichord

accordion

             tambourine
             mandolin

harmonica

             saxophone   lyre

cello
bravo   bugle
violin   an
             bagpipes

guitar

             expert

organ

             castanets

harp
piano

Objective: to extend vocabulary and recognize common nouns.

Weight training

Look at the numbers on the weights. Either half or double the numbers as shown. Write the answers on the weights, as in the first picture.

Objective: practice in multiplication and division.

Word games!

Can you finish each word with the right word-ending?

ail	ale	ane	ain
p _ _ _	p _ _ _	c _ _ _ _	t _ _ _ _
s _ _ _	s _ _ _	m _ _ _	m _ _ _
t _ _ _	s _ _ _ _	c _ _ _	s _ _ _ _
s _ _ _ _	g _ _ _	l _ _ _	d _ _ _ _

Here are some words where the letters have been jumbled up. Can you unscramble the letters and write the words?

airdo ....   noymek ....   macine ....

difren ....   grite ....   hoylaid ....

aptyr ....   danpa ....   jeyorun ....

Can you find eight animals which can be kept as pets in this wordsearch puzzle?

B	U	D	G	E	R	I	G	A	R
G	U	I	N	E	A	P	I	G	A
D	B	U	D	G	B	I	C	A	T
O	D	G	E	R	B	B	A	R	I
G	O	L	D	F	I	S	H	D	A
A	H	A	M	S	T	E	R	R	T

Objective: to develop and improve spelling and vocabulary.

Past and future

 Here is a story written in the future tense. Can you put it in the past tense? Beware - the verbs must be right and the story has to make sense!

During the summer holidays next year, John will go with his Mum and Dad to a camp-site. They will pitch their tent then get to know their fellow-campers. John will make lots of new friends. Together they will go to the theme park and every day they will go walking or swimming in the lake on the camp-site. They will have lots of fun and John will have a wonderful holiday. Then, once he returns home, he will write long letters to his new friends.

....

....

....

....

....

....

....

....

Write a short letter to a friend telling him or her about your last holiday.

....

....

....

....

Objective: to convert from future to past tense.

At the theme park

123 Write the missing numbers on these rope ladders.

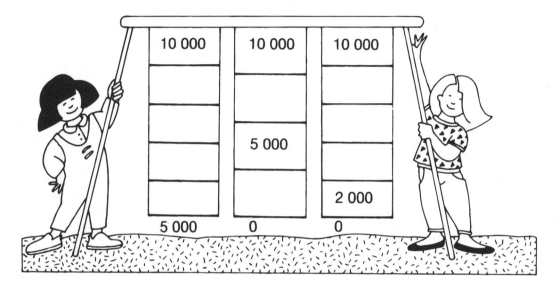

123 Put these numbers in order, starting with the smallest and ending with the largest.

9 000   15 000   56 000   24 000   13 000   21 000

....

123 Write the missing numbers on the swing-boats to complete the number sequences.

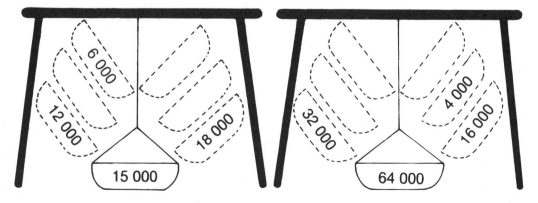

Objective: practice in basic mathematical skills.

Beginnings of words

 The beginning of each word has been left out. Can you write the correct one to complete the word? You can use a dictionary to help you.

pro-/pre-/pri-

_ _ _ posal	_ _ _ vate	_ _ _ vent
_ _ _ ncipal	_ _ _ spect	_ _ _ tend
_ _ _ view	_ _ _ nting	_ _ _ spect
_ _ _ claim	_ _ _ mrose	_ _ _ sume

in/im/un

_ _ correct	_ _ helpful	_ _ proper
_ _ mask	_ _ direct	_ _ visible
_ _ postor	_ _ beaten	_ _ breakable
_ _ possible	_ _ human	_ _ perfect

gn/kn

_ _ aw	_ _ ow	_ _ ight
_ _ ock	_ _ ot	_ _ ew
_ _ ot	_ _ ome	_ _ ash
_ _ u	_ _ itting	_ _ at

sc/sk

_ _ oop	_ _ ooter	_ _ ip
_ _ rimp	_ _ ies	_ _ ale
_ _ ate	_ _ unk	_ _ ary
_ _ ill	_ _ ull	_ _ arf

in
im
gn
pro
pre
pri
sk
kn
un
sc

Objective: to improve spelling and recognize similar-sounding word beginnings.

Angles and groups

 How many angles can you count in each shape? Write the number on the dotted line.

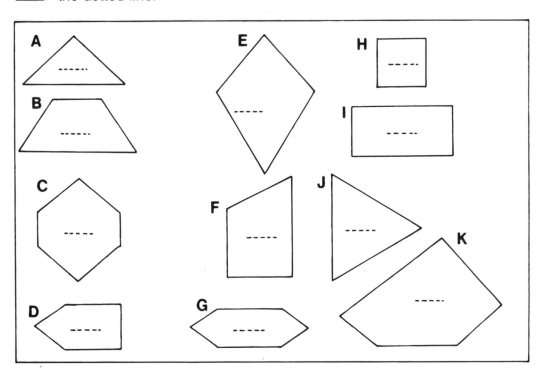

Put the shapes in the correct group.

L = (shapes with 3 angles)   N = (shapes with 5 angles)
M = (shapes with 4 angles)   O = (shapes with 6 angles)

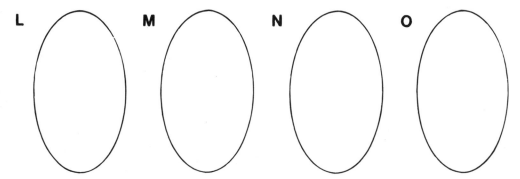

Objective: to distinguish geometric shapes and to complete a diagram.

Objects in sentences

 Complete these sentences by writing in the missing objects. The object in the first sentence has been underlined.

Can you see the two <u>girls</u>?

Jane is holding a .... in her hands.

She gives her friend a ....

Jane is wearing a pretty ....

Sarah does not have an ....

'Thank you!' she says to ....

Can you see the .... ?

He is wearing .... on his coat.

He has .... in his hand.

He is going to cut the ....

The lady wears a .... on her head.

'I declare this .... open!' she says.

Can you see the .... ?

He looks down at the ....

He has put on his ....

He goes down the ....

He has a .... on his face.

He holds .... in his hands.

Can you see the .... ?

He has not woken the ....

He has taken all the ....

He is carrying a .... in his hand.

A mask hides his ....

He creeps through the ....

Objective: to recognize the direct object in grammatical structure.

Decimal numbers

Can you do the sums in each small picture?

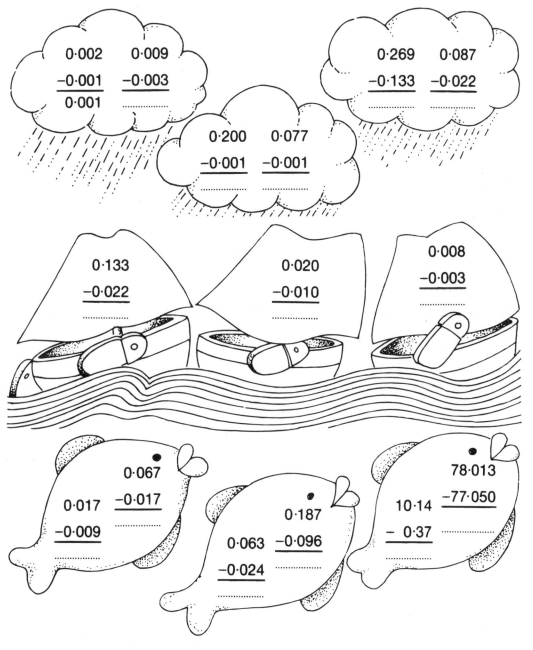

$$0.002 \quad 0.009$$
$$-0.001 \quad -0.003$$
$$\overline{0.001} \quad \text{.......}$$

$$0.269 \quad 0.087$$
$$-0.133 \quad -0.022$$
$$\text{.......} \quad \text{.......}$$

$$0.200 \quad 0.077$$
$$-0.001 \quad -0.001$$
$$\text{.......} \quad \text{.......}$$

$$0.133$$
$$-0.022$$
$$\text{.......}$$

$$0.020$$
$$-0.010$$
$$\text{.......}$$

$$0.008$$
$$-0.003$$
$$\text{.......}$$

$$0.067$$
$$-0.017$$
$$\text{.......}$$

$$0.017$$
$$-0.009$$
$$\text{.......}$$

$$0.187$$
$$0.063 \quad -0.096$$
$$-0.024 \quad \text{.......}$$
$$\text{.......}$$

$$78.013$$
$$-77.050$$
$$10.14 \quad \text{.......}$$
$$- \ 0.37$$

Objective: practice in basic maths skills using decimal numbers.

Participles

 A participle is one part of a verb in the future or a past tense eg. she had **written**, he will **write**. Underline the participle in each sentence.

Long, long ago, rats had invaded a town. One day, a strange man had appeared. By playing a magic pipe, he had succeeded in leading the rats to a river, where they had drowned. 'I refuse to give you the reward I promised!' the mayor had said. Next time the man had begun to play, all the children had followed him into a cave. The entrance had closed and the children had gone for ever.

 Change these sentences into questions.

He had eaten every one of the cakes.

....

She was never naughty again in school.

....

Never had I imagined such a wonderful sight.

....

You have not been able to find your toys in your room.

....

You have not finished tidying all your toys away.

....

Objective: recognizing participles of verbs; writing in the interrogative.

Empty bottles

Can you do the multiplication sums on this page? Write the answers on the dotted lines. Then add the two together and write the total.

Objective: practice in multiplication and addition.

A bunch of flowers

Find the words which are hidden on these flowers. The first three letters of each word are written below.

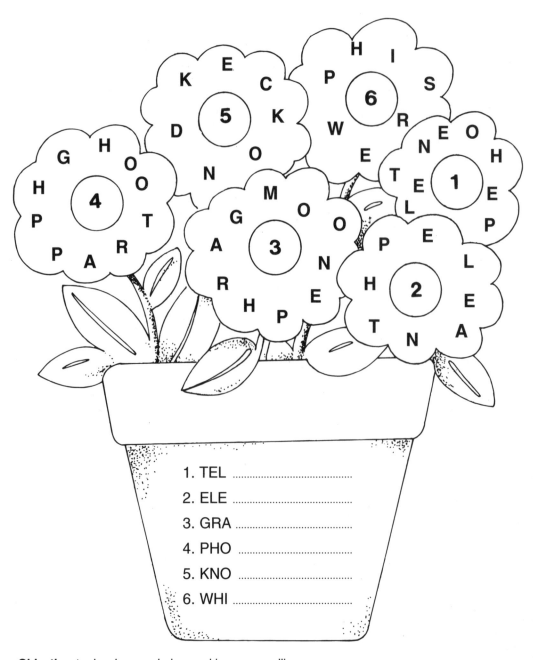

1. TEL ....
2. ELE ....
3. GRA ....
4. PHO ....
5. KNO ....
6. WHI ....

Objective: to develop vocabulary and improve spelling.

At the swimming pool!

 Measure the area of the swimming pool.

Use the following formula to find the area of a square or rectangle:-

length x breadth

So the area of the swimming pool is

....

 Find the area of the surface shaded in black in each diagram. Write the answer on the dotted line.

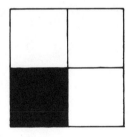

....

....

....

....

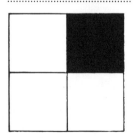

....

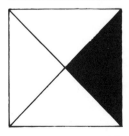

....

Objective: to measure and to calculate area measurement.

Help!

 Join each part of a word to the right word ending!

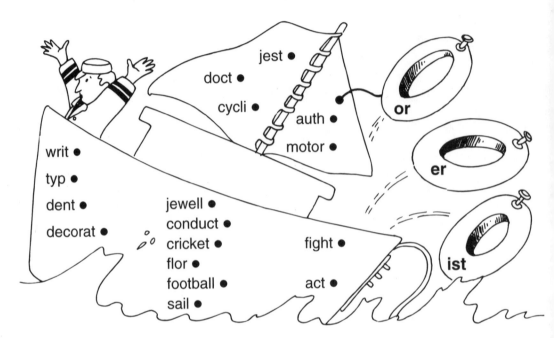

jest •
doct •
cycli •
auth •
motor •

writ •
typ •
dent •
decorat •

jewell •
conduct •
cricket •
flor •
football •
sail •

fight •
act •

or

er

ist

 Write in the correct vowels (a, e, i, o, u) to complete these words.

t r _ _ n	b _ c y c l _	l _ g h t
h _ _ s _	s h _ d	g _ l d f _ s h
c h _ _ r	g _ r d _ n	b _ t h _
p _ _ n t	f _ _ n t _ _ n	s c _ _ t _ r
w _ n d _ w	t _ b l _	p _ c n _ c
d _ n k _ y	t r _ c t _ r	m _ r r _ r
h _ l _ d _ y	b _ l l _ _ n	s _ _ t c _ s _
c _ m p _ t _ r	s _ x _ p h _ n _	c _ m _ l
t h _ _ g h t	c _ _ g h t	t _ l _ p h _ n _
d _ v _ s _ _ n	s t r _ _ n _ r	s _ t c h _ l

Objective: to increase vocabulary and develop correct spelling.

Make a pattern!

These shapes can turn both clockwise and anti-clockwise. Complete the series.

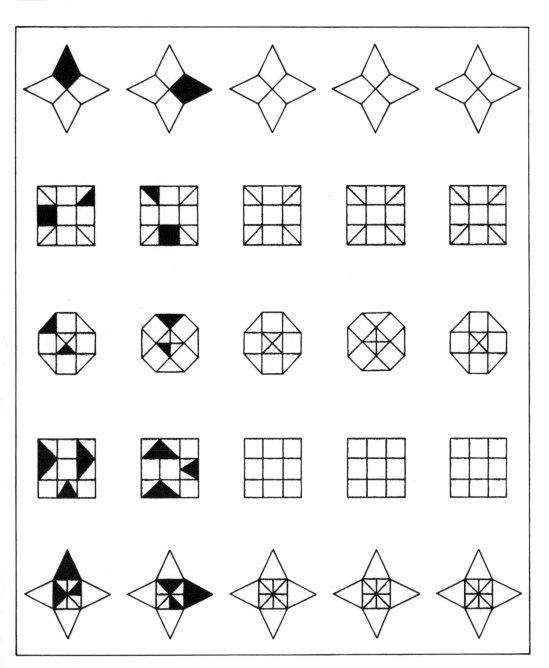

Objective: to develop reasoning and logic.

Opposites

Here are some adjectives (describing words). Find their opposite by adding a prefix (a beginning), as in the first example.

possible	impossible
certain	_ _certain
visible	_ _visible
perfect	_ _perfect
definite	_ _definite
comfortable	_ _comfortable
happy	_ _happy
patient	_ _patient
sufficient	_ _sufficient
likely	_ _likely

Make sentences using the following words in two different ways. The first example has been done for you.

rose   The girl picked a rose for her mother.

The man rose from his chair.

match ....

....

chop ....

....

sweet ....

....

light ....

....

Objective: recognition of adjectives and development of vocabulary.

Division sums

A few more division sums for you to do! The first one has been completed for you.

```
      9881
 3 | 29643
     27
     26
     24
      24
      24
      03
       3
       0
```

5 | 18575

6 | 29562

7 | 11543

Objective: practice in division.

On the telephone

 Mark and James are talking on the telephone. What do you think James might say?

Mark: Hi, James! How are you today?

James: ....

Mark: Are you going swimming this afternoon?

James: ....

Mark: You'll have time to do that when you get back.

James: ....

Mark: You can borrow that from your brother! He won't say anything!

James: ....

Mark: It won't take you that long to get your things together! Come on, hurry up! We're going to be late.

James: ....

Now answer the following questions.

Where would you look for a telephone number? ....

What must you know in order to find out someone's telephone number?

....

Write the telephone numbers of your best friends below.

....

Objective: writing dialogue and researching information.

The football match

 This exercise is about seeing what people have in common and making groups.

David (d), Bernard (b), Mark (m) Lucy (l), Eric (e), William (w) and Jeff (j) are watching a football match.

Circle B = children with a hooter
Circle C = children with a flag
Circle D = children wearing a bobble-hat

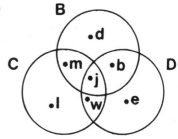

 Try answering these questions. Two have been answered for you.

What do you know about David? David has a hooter.

What do you know about Bernard? ....

What do you know about Mark? ....

What do you know about Lucy? ....

What do you know about Eric? ....

What do you know about William? William has a flag and a bobble-hat.

What do you know about Jeff? ....

Who only wears a bobble-hat? ....

Who has a bobble-hat and a flag? ....

Objective: to understand the concept of groups.

A little story

 Come up with a title for this little story. Then write or underline the words which best summarize the story.

Stanley has a fox which he keeps as a pet. One day, the fox escaped and followed him to school. It jumped through the window during a history lesson. How the children laughed!

....

 Now you tell a story. You will find the theme inside the chest! Use the words written inside the little boxes.

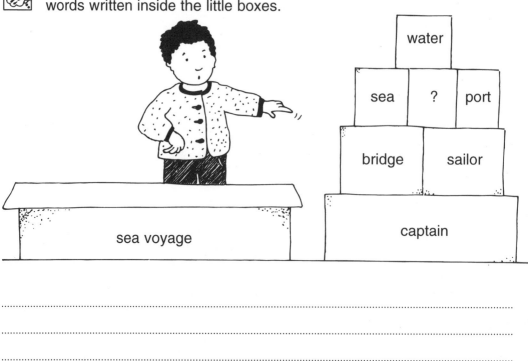

water

sea ? port

bridge sailor

captain

sea voyage

....
....
....
....
....

Objective: to recognize key words and write a story on a given theme.

Washing lines

Can you do the sums on the clothes hanging out to dry? Then add the answers together and write the total on the basket.

7·235
−3·488
....

6·117
−2·558
....

19·268
−16·324
....

98·056
−17·267
....

.... + ... + ... + ... =

21·670
− 2·994
....

19·776
−18·989
....

23·716
−17·618
....

14·281
− 3·087
....

.... + ... + ... + ... =

Objective: to calculate decimal numbers.

Groups of words

 Can you split up each sentence into groups of words? The first one has been done for you. Then underline the verbs (doing words).

The monkey / jumped / from roof to roof / with lots of ease.

The children showed us their red balloons.

Anne baked an enormous cake for her mother's birthday.

The mayor cut his finger during the opening ceremony.

Despite everything, the teacher was still frightened of the little fox.

Then the clown pushed his friend into the water.

At the zoo the chimpanzees did lots of tricks for the visitors.

Nobody believed that there was a monster in the wood.

You can see two parrots high up there in the trees.

As night fell, danger threatened the rescuers high up on the mountain-side.

Suddenly, in one enormous leap, the beast came out of his lair.

He had done everything to avoid the fatal blow.

Do you know how he escaped last time?

He turned himself into a bird with a wave of his magic wand.

 Read these four sentences carefully and make up other sentences using the same words.

The fox crossed the village square at full speed.

....

The policemen were amazed by such a sight.

....

The people had a good laugh when they heard the story.

....

Why don't we go to the cinema tomorrow afternoon?

....

Objective: to divide sentences into subject, verb and object.

Part of the total

123 Look at the black part in each square. What proportion is this of the whole square? Study the example first.

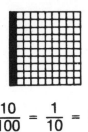

$$\frac{10}{100} = \frac{1}{10} = 0{\cdot}1 \qquad \frac{}{100} = \frac{}{10} = \text{.....} \qquad \frac{}{100} = \text{.....} \qquad \frac{}{100} = \text{.....}$$

$$\frac{}{100} = \frac{}{10} = \text{.....} \qquad \frac{}{100} = \text{.....} \qquad \frac{}{100} = \frac{}{10} = \text{.....} \qquad \frac{}{100} = \text{.....}$$

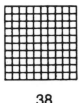 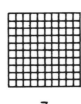

$$\frac{}{100} = \frac{}{10} = \text{.....} \qquad \frac{}{100} = \text{.....} \qquad \frac{}{100} = \text{.....} \qquad \frac{}{100} = \text{.....}$$

123 Colour in black the fraction indicated beneath each square.

$$\frac{38}{100} \qquad\qquad \frac{7}{10} \qquad\qquad \frac{2}{10} \qquad\qquad \frac{12}{100}$$

Objective: understanding the concept of and working with fractions.

Be original!

 Can you make up sentences using the two words in each balloon?

Julie is knitting a lovely jumper.

car
keys

....

trees
wood

....

books
library

....

words
dictionary

....

horse
stable

....

rabbit
warren

....

Objective: making sentences including given words.

The Cossack dance

Can you do the sum written on the costume of each Cossack dancer?

2390
+ 80

3750
+ 20

8750
+180

3720
+660

8430
−5210

7570
−6210

3980
−780

6000
−4190

2190
× 3

3580
× 2

1850
× 4

Objective: exercise in addition, subtraction and multiplication.

All change!

 Change all these sentences into questions. Be sure that all your questions make sense!

Brian fed seed to the birds.

....

Athens is the capital city of Greece.

....

George Washington was the first president of the USA.

....

An old hippopotamus looked at us.

....

At night, the cat ran into the shed.

....

The owl flew past us very quickly.

....

Change these sentences into the negative (saying not or no).

They walked across the field at midday.
They did not walk across the field at midday.

She told me a funny story.

....

The fawn stopped being frightened of people.

....

Our dog had chased three hares.

....

How can you give away that lovely toy?

....

Objective: to construct sentences in the interrogative and negative.

Number puzzles

 Try this puzzle. Instead of writing letters, you write numbers in the squares.

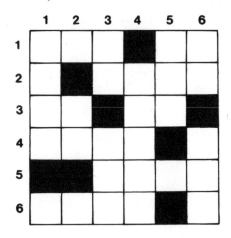

Across
1. Days in a year/one dozen.
2. 2 x 1 = ... / 4 x 662 = ...
3. One year and 4 weeks = ... weeks
   2 days and 6 hours = ... hours
4. The first four even numbers/
   The largest single numeral
5. 3.416 kg = ... g
6. 2468 - 34 = ...

Down
1. 32.52 litres = ... cl / 1 x 2 = ...
2. Two trios .... / 256 ÷ 4 = ... /
   1 x 4 = ...
3. Number of weeks in one year/
   1266 ÷ 2 = ...
4. 16461 x 4 = ...
5. 12 x 12 = ... / 2, 3, 4, 5
6. 4 weeks = ... days /
   107 x 9 = ...

 Now write the correct numbers below.

a quarter of a year =................... months	2 quarters = ... half
half a dozen = ...	6 halves = ... quarters
3 leap years = ...days	1 metre = ... cms
4 years = ... months	6 halves = ... thirds
20 weeks =.. days	1 hour = ... minutes

Objective: to calculate and to learn numerical terms.

Proverbs

Can you join up each proverb with its meaning in everyday language?

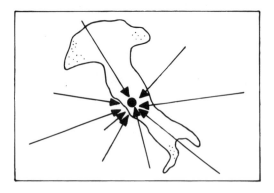

One swallow does not make a summer. * * Anything can be done if you believe in it enough.

All roads lead to Rome. * * Troubles always come together.

All that glitters is not gold. * * Early success does not always last.

It takes a thief to catch a thief. * * A good beginning is a great help.

Well begun is half done. * * Leave well alone.

It's no good crying over spilt milk. * * One rogue recognizes another.

Faith can move mountains. * * There can be many ways of doing something.

It never rains but it pours. * * Appearances can be deceptive.

Let sleeping dogs lie. * * There is usually some cause for a rumour.

A stitch in time saves nine. * * It's no good fretting about something which cannot be put right.

There is no smoke without fire. * * Quick action may save a lot of trouble later on.

Objective: to learn the meanings of proverbs.

Parachute jump

Can you do these division sums? Write your answers on the parachutes.

$\frac{3}{4} \div 10 = \frac{3}{40}$

$\frac{1}{2} \div 10 =$ ....

$\frac{4}{6} \div 100 =$ ....

$\frac{12}{15} \div 5 =$ ....

$\frac{2}{4} \div 1000 =$ ....

$\frac{7}{8} \div 10 =$ ....

$\frac{12}{16} \div 4 =$ ....

$\frac{3}{7} \div 100 =$ ....

Objective: practice in division.

What are they made of?

 What is each object made of?

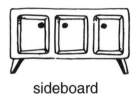

ring   shoe   sideboard

a box made of *wood*   a chain made of...

a wallet made of ....   a strap made of ....

a coin made of ....   a door made of ....

a chair made of ....   a necklace made of ....

a shoe made of ....   a hat made of ....

a bag made of..   a picture frame made of ....

a bracelet made of ....   a locket made of ....

a rafter made of...   a table made of ....

a crown made of ....   a statue made of ....

 Do you know where we get these materials from?

gold is extracted from a mine   coal is ....

wood is ....   petrol is ....

paper is ....   oil is ....

iron is ....   stone is ....

leather is ....   clay is ....

oak is ....   brick is ....

bread is ....   wool is ....

cardboard is ....   slate is ....

Objective: creative thinking.

Count up the points!

 Can you help the teacher to add up all the points scored by his class?

All the children have received their exam results. Here are the results.
Peter and three other boys made only 3 mistakes.
Four boys and one girl made 6 mistakes.
Anne and Verity only made 2 mistakes.
As always, Sally did not make any mistakes!
What is the average mark out of 10 for the class?
(Add all the points together then divide by the number of students.)
Deduct one point for each mistake.

Method and answer ....

....

....

 Now look at the table below. Can you work out the average
temperature in the morning and at midday?

	8 h.	12h.
Monday	12°	15°
Tuesday	16°	25°
Wednesday	13°	20°
Thursday	11°	19°
Friday	10°	18°
Saturday	12°	24°
Sunday	15°	28°

Average morning temperature ....

Average temperature at midday ....

Objective: to learn to calculate averages.

At the supermarket

 Look at the pictures on this page. Can you make up a funny story about them?

....

....

....

....

....

....

....

....

Objective: to write a story following a sequence of pictures.

More sums!

In great-grandfather's attic, Jack found a piece of paper with different sums written on it. Can you do them?

816·79	675·385	420·357
+615·837	+ 67·53	+218·652

218·513	62·718	917·560
+ 7·62	+335·133	+ 38·51

716·18	119·227	17·67
+ 76·59	+ 86·816	+13·24

125·630	108·720	978·37
+ 40·410	+ 8·69	+ 20·2

569·23	634·16
+318·15	+ 33·49

Objective: basic maths skills in decimal numerals.

Root verbs

A verb is a 'doing' word. A noun is the name of something. Some nouns are based on verbs. Write a noun after the infinitive verb (see the example.)

to work	work
to decide	decision
to open	....
to live	....
to prove	....
to decorate	....
to understand	....
to prepare	....
to compete	....
to protect	....

Now find the infinitive verb on which the noun is based. You can use a dictionary to help you.

distinction	to distinguish
painting	....
departure	....
freedom	....
presentation	....
ending	....
beginning	....
protection	....
sleep	....
dance	....
photograph	....

Objective: to recognize the link between derivative nouns and the infinitive verb.

Weather forecast

You can be a weather expert! Just try putting the right information on the weather chart!

Check the temperature each day for a month. Write down the wind direction, if the sky is cloudy, if it is rainy, or if there is a mist, a storm, sunshine, etc. At the end you will have a record of one month's weather. Be sure to check your weather facts at the same time each day.

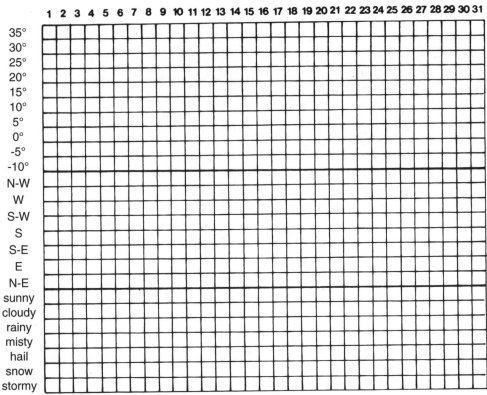

Objective: to record information on a chart.

Just imagine...

What two words do you first think of when you see each picture? See the first example.

orchard   ....

nature   ....

....

....

....

....

Objective: to understand the concept of word association.

From the smallest to the largest

123 Reduce each fraction by the same denominator (figure below the line). Write them on the dolls, starting with the smallest and ending with the largest.

$\frac{18}{4}$ $\frac{7}{2}$ $\frac{22}{4}$ $\frac{15}{5}$ $\frac{8}{10}$ $=$ $\frac{18}{4} = 4\frac{2}{4} = 4\frac{1}{2}$ $\frac{7}{2} = 3\frac{1}{2}$

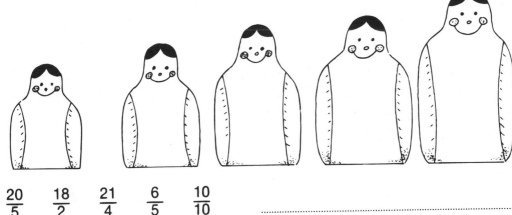

$\frac{20}{5}$ $\frac{18}{2}$ $\frac{21}{4}$ $\frac{6}{5}$ $\frac{10}{10}$ ....

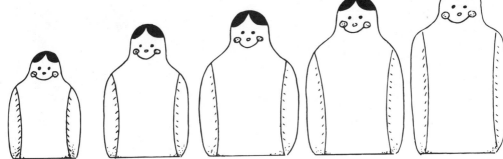

123 Now try these sums.

$\frac{10}{3} \div 10 =$ ....

$\frac{8}{6} + \frac{2}{6} =$ ....

$\frac{1}{8} \times 128 =$ ....

$\frac{4}{3} \times 7 =$ ....

$\frac{9}{8} \div 3 =$ ....

$\frac{1}{4} \times 640 =$ ....

$\frac{12}{4} \times 8 =$ ....

$\frac{21}{3} \div 7 =$ ....

$\frac{1}{8} \times 160 =$ ....

Objective: working with fractions.

Which book?

 Think of a book which you have read recently. What can you remember about it?

Title ....

Author(s) ....

Illustrator ....

Publisher ....

Central character ....

Other characters in the story ....

Number of chapters ....

What sort of book is it? ....

Write a short summary of the book.

....

....

....

....

....

....

Why did you like the book?

....

....

....

....

....

Objective: learning to appraise a book and to write about it.

Reflections in a mirror

 Draw these pictures as if they were reflected in a mirror. The artist has shown you how to begin.

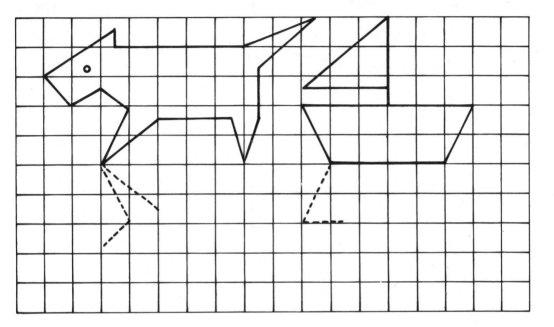

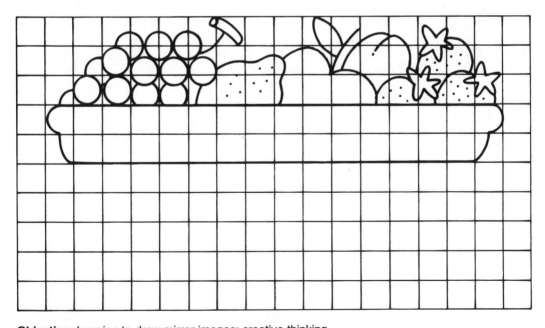

Objective: learning to draw mirror images; creative thinking.

Prepositions

A preposition shows the relationship between two things - *Tom is in the garden.* Finish off each sentence after the preposition, using the examples as a guide.

In front of the house there is a road.
Beside the house there is a garden.
Inside the house, mother is cooking a meal.
Behind the house there flows a stream.

In front of ....

Beside ....

Inside ....

Behind ....

In front of ....

Beside ....

Inside ....

Behind ....

Here is a list of prepositions! Which one belongs in each sentence?
with, at, for, from, to, into, of, by

Paul was angry _____ his little sister.

The man called _____ assistance..

The fishermen were alarmed _____ the news of bad weather.

'I am getting impatient _____ having to wait!' said the mayor.

The teacher was going _____ the classroom.

The children went _____ the seaside.

The train departed _____ the station.

The cat was fond _____ her basket.

Objective: to recognize prepositions and to use them correctly.

Shapes

Look carefully at all the shapes on this page, then answer the questions.

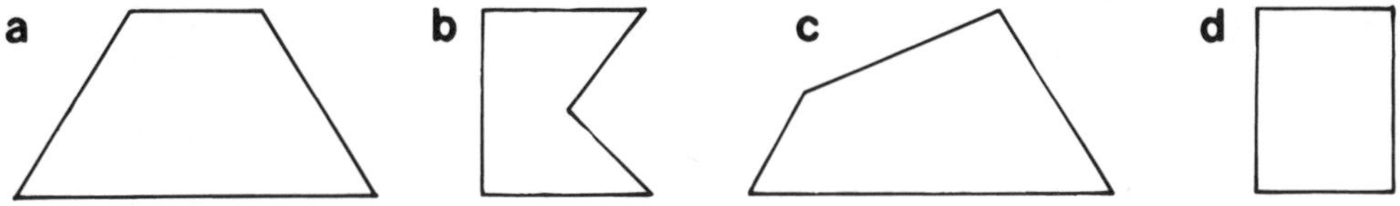

a   b   c   d

Which of the shapes above is a trapezium?

A trapezium is a .... with two sides .... length.

The other two sides are not equal. These sides are ....to each

other.

Complete the following to make four parallelograms. Use your ruler and your protractor or set square. Then, guess which shape is described below.

a   b   c   d

It is a parallelogram. It has four right angles and its opposite sides are equal

to each other. The two diagonals are equal in length and cut each other in

half.

Complete the following to make three diamond shapes. Then, finish off the sentences at the bottom of the page.

A diamond is a .... with four .... sides.

It has .... sides and four .... The angles are

Objective: to recognize and define geometric figures.

Make some sentences!

 Make proper sentences using the words which are given, and you will write a little story. The title is written on the rocks.

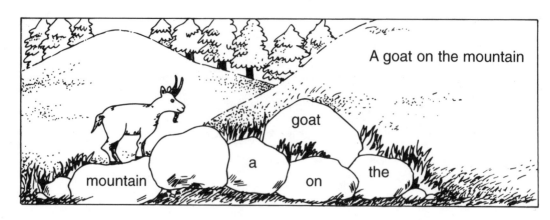

a mountain climbed up goat a high little

....

queen treated her just the like a animals

....

was the mountain thought the wonderful simply goat

....

delicious the tasted which grew all around green grass

....

some the one goat heard leaves rustling loudly night

....

the of gleamed in wolf the eyes enormous darkness an

....

the all animals the it wolf until fled fought mountain the

....

had the goat by its new friends little been saved

....

Objective: construction of sentences in correct sequence.

All fresh bread!

How much is each loaf? Do the sums and see!

$$\begin{array}{r} 4260 \\ \times\ \ 3 \\ \hline {---}8- \end{array}$$

$$\begin{array}{r} 32\_0 \\ \times\ \ 7 \\ \hline --\ 54\ -- \end{array}$$

$$\begin{array}{r} 4\_12 \\ \times\ \ - \\ \hline 17248 \end{array}$$

$$\begin{array}{r} \_\ 86\ \_ \\ \times\ \ 3 \\ \hline 23\ \_80 \end{array}$$

$$\begin{array}{r} \_\ 45\ \_ \\ \times\ \ 2 \\ \hline 18900 \end{array}$$

$$\begin{array}{r} 35\_0 \\ \times\ \ 6 \\ \hline ---\ 0\ - \end{array}$$

$$\begin{array}{r} 6430 \\ \times\ \ - \\ \hline --\ 010 \end{array}$$

$$\begin{array}{r} 8920 \\ \times\ \ 8 \\ \hline ----- \end{array}$$

$$\begin{array}{r} 4860 \\ \times\ \ 4 \\ \hline ----- \end{array}$$

$$\begin{array}{r} 8760 \\ \times\ \ 2 \\ \hline ----- \end{array}$$

$$\begin{array}{r} 3970 \\ \times\ \ 7 \\ \hline ----- \end{array}$$

Objective: exercises in multiplication.

Crossword

Can you do this crossword puzzle?

Across
1. Yearly.
2. The husband of a Countess (or calculate numbers).
   Masculine pronoun.
3. Short dress worn for ballet practice.
   Shortened form of 'Daddy'.
4. Opposite of 'out'.
   Past tense of 'to speed'.
5. Green feathery plant, often used in wreaths and bouquets.
6. Present tense of 'to do'.
   I am going - - the park.
7. I'd like - - apple.
   Opposite of high.
8. Next number to one.
   Short preposition.

Objective: creative thinking.

Down
1. Pretending. Actors do this for a living.
2. A .... is the name of something.
   Expression of disappointment. Rhymes with 'raw'.
3. Hard fruit (or something which goes with a bolt).
   Opposite of 'yes'.
4. New.
5. Preposition. I sat . . my desk.
   Pushes or pokes.
6. Name of a lion's home.
7. Past tense of 'to have'.
   Another word for 'also' .
8. This colour means 'stop'.
   Opposite of 'up'.

Keep counting!

Find the way to the lake by taking the path where the numbers follow on. (• = 1 and —— = 5). Colour the right path in yellow.

• = 1
—— = 5

Objective: application of logic and reasoning.

About pollution....

 Read the following passage carefully.

Pollution is when something pure is spoilt by people. Our environment is becoming more and more polluted. There are many causes, such as increasing amounts of household rubbish, waste material and litter. Factories and farms are also responsible for pollution. Smoke and gases belch out from factory chimneys and insecticides are sprayed over crops and woodland. There are many types of pollution. The air is polluted by exhaust fumes from cars, lorries and all types of traffic. The ozone layer is damaged by the pollution of aerosols and toxic gases from industry. Exhaust waste and rubbish from shipping pollute rivers and seas.

 Now, answer the following questions.

What are the causes of pollution mentioned in this passage? ....
....
....

Can you think of any other causes of pollution? ....
....
....

What can people do to prevent pollution?
....
....

What can **you** do to prevent pollution?
Try to think of more than one thing.

....
....
....

Objective: comprehension and creative thinking.

Believe and receive!

 Lots of words end in 'ieve'. Here is a rhyme to help you remember the right spelling -

i before e, except after c. When a word begins with c, the *e* comes before the *i.*
Can you fill in the missing letters so that each word is spelt correctly?

'There is a th _ _f up to misch_ _f in this village!' said the Ch _ _ f
Inspector, 'and it is my bel_ _ f that someone has rec_ _ ved some important
information! Do not be dec_ _ ved! We must retr_ _ve the stolen goods and
ach_ _ ve success in this case! A valuable watch, for which there is no
rec_ _pt, is missing! Keys to br_ _f cases have been stolen, and a ring from
a silk handkerch_ _ f!' Just then, the Ch _ _ f Inspector rec_ _ved a
message. The stolen goods had been retr_ _ved in a f_ _ ld! 'I'm rel_ _ ved
to hear that!' he cried. 'So, who was the th_ _ f? A daring robber? A burglar?'
'No, Ch_ _f!' came the reply. 'The th_ _ f was a magpie!'
'I do not bel_ _ ve it!' was all the poor Ch _ _ f Inspector could say!

 All the following words can be found in our wordsearch puzzle.

field, grief, friend, receipt, retrieve, deceive, achieve, shield

S	H	I	E	L	D	R	E	C	E
R	E	C	R	E	C	E	I	P	T
F	I	E	L	D	E	C	E	T	E
G	R	I	E	F	R	I	E	N	D
A	C	H	I	E	V	E	R	E	C
R	E	T	R	I	E	V	E	D	R
E	D	E	C	E	I	V	E	D	D

Objective: to recognize correct spelling.

Anne and the monkey

 Put these sentences in the right order to make a story.

A huge monkey chased after her.
She had a horrible nightmare.
The monkey chased her to a tree.
Anne scrambled up into the tree.
Anne fell to the ground head first.
Anne had a very disturbed night.
But the monkey followed her into the tree.
Phew! It was only a bad dream.
Anne woke up with a start.
It was horrible.

....

....

....

....

....

....

....

....

....

Objective: correct sequencing.

It's a message in the sky!

It's is **only** a short way of writing *It is*, with an apostrophe to show that a letter is missing. Can you say which three of these messages are right and which are wrong?

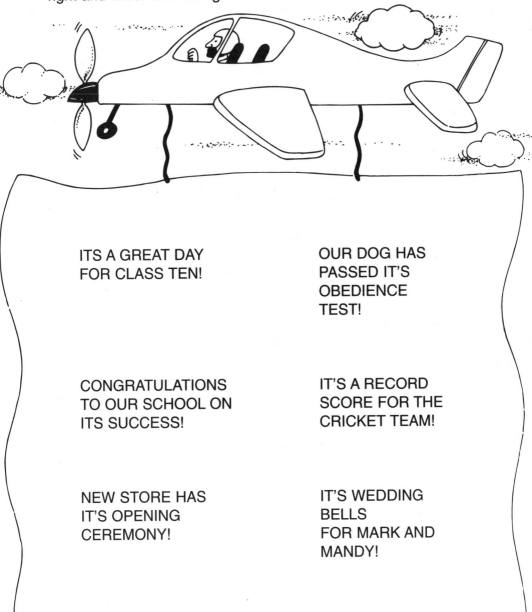

ITS A GREAT DAY
FOR CLASS TEN!

OUR DOG HAS
PASSED IT'S
OBEDIENCE
TEST!

CONGRATULATIONS
TO OUR SCHOOL ON
ITS SUCCESS!

IT'S A RECORD
SCORE FOR THE
CRICKET TEAM!

NEW STORE HAS
IT'S OPENING
CEREMONY!

IT'S WEDDING
BELLS
FOR MARK AND
MANDY!

Objective: to define meaning of contraction.

From the present to the past

These sentences have been written in the present tense. Can you write each one in the past tense?

The monkey sees a lion walking in the woods.

....

He brings a number of presents for each guest.

....

You joke too much in class.

....

After two hours walking, he sits on the bank.

....

Why do Peter and Shelly visit the zoo so often?

....

They come to our house with some friends.

....

Now put these verbs written in the past tense into the infinitive.

I played	(to play)	we ate	....
he went	....	she took	....
you said	....	you thought	....
I did	....	he painted	....
we played	....	they cried	....
he received	....	she swam	....
you made	....	I built	....
I photographed	....	you rescued	....
she waved	....	he was	....
you worried	....	we threw	....

Objective: to learn correct conjugation of verbs in the past tense.

A prisoner in the castle!

If you can do the sums on this page, the princess can escape! Can you help her?

23780
−14620
....

8760
−2380
....

89760
−44980
....

12870
−10720
....

45920
−34710
....

18620
−17890
....

21360
−19990
....

870
−680
....

890
−170
....

18060
−12720
....

970
−520
....

19760
−13680
....

Objective: to practise subtraction.

At the cinema

 Try writing a story using these words:
public, film, suspense, robbers, gold, chase, prison.

....

....

....

....

....

....

....

....

....

....

....

....

Give your views.

Do you sometimes go to the cinema? ....

What is the best film you have ever seen? ....

What is the film about? ....

....

Do you watch a lot of television? ....

What is your favourite programme? ....

Why?

....

....

Objective: learning to write a report and to express an opinion.

Brain teaser!

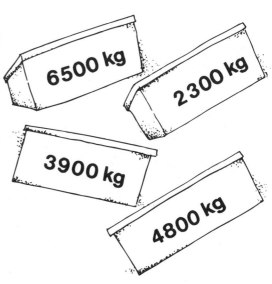

? Read the passage carefully then look at the picture. Both these will help you answer the questions.

Andrew is a lorry driver. His lorry is allowed to take a full load of 20,000 kg or 20 tonnes. The lorry itself weighs 7 tonnes. When Andrew loads all the crates, he has .... kg or .... tonnes in his lorry. Then he drives his lorry on to a special weighing machine to find the total weight. The machine shows .... kg or .... tonnes. Is he allowed to continue with this weight?

6500 kg

2300 kg

3900 kg

4800 kg

? Solve this problem!

On Sunday we collected lots of old newspapers! We split up into three groups. Anna collected 960 kg of paper with four friends. Mary, Jason and Luke collected 580 kg and the last group of four collected 740 kg. How many kg did we collect together? ....
What was the average each of us collected? ....

Objective: to apply logic and reasoning and to calculate averages.

Where is the link-up?

 Join the words which you think go together.

Paris •	• library
piano •	• clock
church •	• capital
station •	• postman
time •	• bell
book •	• swallow
diamond •	• instrument
hotel •	• train
forest •	• bed
bird •	• tree
letter •	• gold

 Join the consonants and the vowels of these two lists to make complete words

N-GHT-NG-L- •	• O-U-E
PH-T-GR-PH •	• A-I-E
C-M-R- •	• O-O-O-I-E
T-L-V-S--N •	• E-E-O-E
T-L-PH-N- •	• E-E-I-I-O
H-L-D-Y •	• E-O-A-I-O
C-MP-T-R •	• I-I-A-E
D-C-R-T--N •	• O-I-A
L-C-M-T-V- •	• A-E-A
M-CH-N- •	• O-O-A

Objective: establishing links between words; spelling practice.

Rules of geometry

 A surveyor must calculate the perimeter and the area of a piece of ground. Could you do this as well?

To calculate the perimeter, add together the length of all the sides. The perimeter of this square is ....

To obtain the area, multiply

.... x ....

The area of this square is ....

For a square where the sides measure 10 cm or 1 dm:

perimeter is: .... + ... + ... + ... = ... cm

area is : .... x .... = ... cm2 = ... dm2

123 Complete these equations.

$1 \ dm^2 =$ .... cm^2 $0.25 \ m^2 =$ .... dm^2 $4.08 \ m^2 =$ .... cm^2

$6 \ m^2 =$ .... dm^2 $0.50 \ m^2 =$ .... dm^2 $12.2 \ m^2 =$ .... dm^2

$3.75 \ m^2 =$ .... dm^2 $2.15 \ dm^2 =$ .... cm^2 $20.6 \ m^2 =$ .... dm^2

$0.17 \ m^2 =$ .... dm^2 $0.1 \ m^2 =$ .... dm^2 $0.12 \ dm^2 =$ .... cm^2

$0.01 \ m^2 =$ .... dm^2 $0.7 \ m^2 =$ .... dm^2 $100 \ m^2 =$ .... cm^2

Objective: practice in calculating perimeter and area.

Find the mistakes!

Read the passage carefully and underline the mistakes. Then re-write it correctly below.

There was once a cockrul who had such a beautiful vioce that his master were very proud of he. But one day an artfal fox pounced on the cockrell and carried him off in his mouth! 'Get that fox!' the cockrels owner told his doggs. 'Get him!' But they cold do nothing.
'That man was a terribul master!'

the cockerel told the fox. 'I wish you wood tell him to go away, two!' The fox didnt think twice about it!
'Yes!' him shouted to the owner of the cockrul. 'You stay ther!' Of cause, as soon as he opened his mouth, the cockerel were free! Next moment, the bird has flown into a tree!

Objective: to recognize common mistakes in grammar and spelling.

Say it with flowers

Can you do all the sums in the flower shop and help the florist?

$3600 \div 10 =$ ....
$9 \cdot 70 \div 10 =$ ....
$8 \div 10 =$ ....
$650 \div 10 =$ ....

$1 \cdot 7 \div 10 =$ ....
$247 \div 100 =$ ....
$7 \cdot 6 \div 10 =$ ....
$18 \div 100 =$ ....

$86 \div 10 =$ ....
$3 \cdot 7 \div 100 =$ ....
$906 \div 10 =$ ....

$800 \div 100 =$ ....
$247 \ 3 \div 100 =$ ....
$20 \cdot 6 \div 2 =$ ....

$56 \cdot 16 \div 8 =$ ....
$66 \cdot 006 \div 6 =$ ....
$54 \cdot 9 \div 9 =$ ....
$39 \cdot 45 \div 3 =$ ....
$42000 \div 4$ ....

$39000 \div 3 =$ ....
$25000 \div 100 =$ ....
$34000 \div 5 =$ ....
$56000 \div 8 =$ ....
$36000 \div 10 =$ ....

Objective: practice in division.

Smaller and smaller

 Shorten each sentence by taking out unnecessary words. The following example will show you how it is done.

> During the holidays we often played in the park.
> We often played in the park.
> We played in the park.
> We played.

Every day, he walked his dog in the big park.

....

....

....

Jill picked apples with Peter in the orchard.

....

....

....

Over there, they are spending all day sunbathing on the sand.

....

....

....

The cyclist unwisely came down the hill at top speed.

....

....

....

This evening I am taking the train as soon as I can.

....

....

....

Objective: to break down sentences into phrases and clauses.